Human Being

MARK CHATTERTON

If you could only see yourself as others see you…..

This book is dedicated to all human beings on Planet Earth whatever their nation, tribe, colour, language, creed, belief, social background, age or ability

CONTENTS

HUMAN BEING

Preface

On a planet many light years away from Earth, the leader of a race of highly evolved beings is speaking to his most trusted advisor......

It has come to my vision that there is a planet in the far reaches of the Universe which needs our closest attention. This planet, from my observations seems so unique of all the planets in the Universe that many Beings are flocking there to exist in that planet's Life Forms. They are going to this planet to live and breathe and interact with all the unique ecosystems there.

Your mission, my Trusted One is to make a visit to this planet, which I understand is called "Earth" by the inhabitants. I want you to observe all the Life Forms that live there and see how they interact with each other. Make a report for me and tell me what happens on this planet – what its life forms are like and how they exist with each other. Finally, tell me whether you think it will go the same way as many other planets in the Universe into extinction; or will it start to flourish once more and still have a future?

Introduction

What a mess the world is in.
I wonder who began it?
Don't ask me – I'm only visiting this planet!

I made my visit to Planet Earth during a period of great change, which the dominant life form, the human beings, call the 21st century of the Common Era. I have concentrated my report on these human beings as they seem to be the controllers of the planet and have succeeded in becoming the dominant species. However, I will also look at many other life forms that live on the planet in all the different environments. Some of the things I am going to tell you, you will find incredible to believe; some things you will find difficult to understand; some of the things these humans do you will find amusing; and some things that you see will shock you. Yet what you see is real. This is actually how human beings live and exist on Planet Earth at this present time.

To make it easier for you to understand how life on Planet Earth works, I have gone to various locations on the planet where I have captured different events or happenings that are occurring at a certain time in an "event-capture". This is so that you can see for yourself the kinds of things that human beings are doing during their existence on Planet Earth. At each location I will explain what is going on, so you will be able to understand human beings better.

Before we start looking at human beings, I need to explain a little about Planet Earth – the place where humans and myriads of other life forms exist. As you come into the region of the Universe known as the Milky Way, there is one solar system within it, which contains Planet Earth and several other planets. You will easily notice the Earth planet, as it is a living planet dominated by the colours of green and brown, and blue and white. When you get to its surface there is every conceivable colour and shade to be seen. The green and brown make up the land, whilst the blue is the colour of the water, and the white is the clouds of water vapour that travel in the atmosphere around the Earth.

There is lots of water on this planet, with oxygen gas in the air around the surface. These two things have led to life coming into existence here. The water can be observed mainly on the surface, but it can also be found underground. The first life forms on Planet Earth lived in the water and then came out of the water to produce Earth life in many different and varied forms; most of them are unlike any you will find elsewhere in the Universe.

There are many different life forms that still exist in the water which the humans mainly call "fish". Next, moving about in the air above the planet's surface are other life forms which the humans call birds and insects. Then on the land part of the Earth are many other non-human life-forms which move around on and beneath the surface, which the humans call "animals". Apart from these main species, there are many more sub-species, existing on the planet. Finally, growing out of the Earth's surface you will observe every conceivable type of vegetation, including lichens, mosses, and flowers, as well as plants and trees.

All of these different life forms have their own space on the planet where they exist and move and intermingle with each other. The surface of Planet Earth is also very varied, ranging from lush vegetation and forests in some parts, to barren, lifeless deserts in other areas. Also, the landscape can be full of hills and mountains in some parts, and then in others you will find rivers and lakes on very flat pieces of the land. I will go into more detail about these other life forms and landscapes elsewhere in my report. But first I will tell you about the human beings and how their bodies work.

Let our journey to Planet Earth begin..................

Part 1

Human Body

We are all flesh and blood – just different skin

The first part of my report begins with how the human beings came into existence on the Planet and how their physical body works.

Human Birth

One of the first questions you will be asking is "How do human beings start as a life form?" Well let me show you…..

Location - Liverpool, England: the delivery room in a maternity hospital

Aaa…aargh! The woman cried out in agony. "aaargh!!!" This time the second scream was even louder; even more intense. "Just one more push, Mrs Walker. Puuush!" At that very moment an eight pound four ounce human baby boy entered the world.. The mother immediately began to relax and the adrenalin of a new and exciting experience started to flow through her aching body. "You've got a healthy baby boy, Mrs Walker. Well done!" The midwife handed over the bundle of red, white and blue flesh to his mother, whilst his father looked proudly on. He wiped a tear from his eye and kissed his wife on her forehead. "What are you going to call him?" asked the midwife. "Adam" replied the father above the howls of the baby boy. Human Life was just starting for this baby……

In this very first event-capture that I am showing to you, you can observe the very start of human life. A human being comes into the world through a process which the humans call "birth". In this process a new human life is created by the transfer of life giving energies between two different humans. You can observe here that humans have different shapes and sizes. In fact, there are two basic human types – Male human and Female human, whereas our race is just one version. Each human type carries different energies, which when combined, create a new human being. The human being thus created can be either male or female, though it is the female human who carries the new human inside her body, until it is time for it to be born.

The human being that is born from the human woman is called a "baby". It has been created by the male version or "man" transferring his life force energy into the female version or "woman" to create this new human being. The man is called the baby's "father", whilst the woman is called the baby's "mother". The baby will be known as their "son" in this case, or if it had been a female baby it would be called a "daughter". This human life form will have spent the last nine Earth months growing and developing into a human body, getting ready for this important event, which all human beings celebrate. They will remember the day that they were born as a human being as their "birthday".

Of course, the human baby is not yet a fully developed human being and is quite helpless at first, being dependent on energy from its mother to survive and grow. It will take around another twenty Earth years for this human baby to go through several different stages of development before it becomes a fully-fledged human being. If you ever visit the Earth, you will see humans of different sizes. The smallest humans are the babies as you have just seen. Then those humans who are slightly bigger and still growing are called "children". Then finally there are humans which are fully grown, who are called "adults". I will go into more detail about these differences later on in my report.

Each human body however carries the same life giving aspects, which is called "DNA" by the humans. Within this life force will be different traits and behaviours which it gets from both its father and its mother, which give it a unique perspective on human life. This will make it completely different from all the other human beings on Earth, even though there are actually billions of human beings living here. However, all human beings do possess many similar parts and workings, about which I will now explain.

The Human Body

Virtually all human beings have the same basic features. These are all parts of the human "body" which is designed for movement and development on the Earth. We don't move in the same way as humans do with our bodies, as ours are much lighter and carry a higher frequency energy compared to the human body. In fact, you will find that human beings move around the Earth much slower than we would do on our home planet.

Location – Chester, England: a suburban house

The little boy was almost two years old, yet he was so different from the baby boy he'd started out in life as. He now had lovely golden locks of hair on his head and his blue eyes shone with innocence. He was now starting to shed the baby fat that he had accumulated and he could now walk, though he was not that steady on his feet. He had started to grow his baby teeth and he was beginning to form sounds and the occasional word with his mouth and vocal chords. He knew the words "Mama", "Dada" and even his own name, Adam. His curiosity knew no bounds and he was now literally "into everything". It was a good job that he knew the command "No!", when he was not allowed to touch something or go somewhere which he didn't realise was dangerous. He also knew when his favourite TV programmes were transmitting on the big screen in front of him. Adam would silently go and sit on his tiny chair and be entranced with the wealth of colour and sounds that were displayed before his eyes.
In another year he would be a different person yet again, as he started to evolve into a child. Then in a few more years' time he would be a teenager with all the hang-ups and angst that those years bring. Then finally one day in the future he would

be fully grown and an adult at last. He would resemble his father in looks but would have many of the mannerisms of his mother. Yet as a human being he was unique, with his own mind and his own way of doing things, reacting to all the sights, sounds and influences all around him.

From this event-capture you will be able to see how the shape of the human being's body is starting to change from the baby you saw earlier into a small human body. Let us now see how the human body works.

The main part of the human body is called the "torso", and this contains most of the parts that make the body work. These parts include the major organs including the "heart", the "lungs", the "liver", the "stomach", the "intestines" and many other parts. These are all interconnected by a series of nerves and vessels carrying a red liquid called "blood", which is part of the living process for human beings. All these parts are held up by a frame of bones which the human beings call the "skeleton".

Attached to the torso at the side are two "arms" connected to "hands" at the other end. Under the torso are two "legs" with "feet" on the end of these. The feet and legs are what make the human being different to other animals as human beings only have two legs and two feet with which they walk on. They are able to stand upright and straight as opposed to the other animals. Virtually all other animals on Planet Earth have four or more legs and feet for movement. There are some exceptions to this such as the Apes and Monkeys, who do stand upright like humans, but they move with the help of their arms and hands.

The arms and hands on the humans are very important to them, as they are used in more complex movements which other animals are not able to achieve. It is the "fingers" and "thumbs" on their hands which help them to touch and grip objects. Over time this has led to human beings developing such skills as writing and drawing, as well as the cutting, shaping and modelling of various objects which they have created.

If we move now to the area on top of the torso, there is an oval shaped container called the "head". This has "ears" on either side of it, which allow sound waves to enter the body. The front part of the head is called the "face". This has two "eyes", which help the human being to see outwards from inside the body. These can be different colours such as green, blue or brown. Then there is a "nose" and a "mouth" which are openings for the Earth gases to move into and out of the body. So "oxygen" enters into the human body and "carbon dioxide" leaves it. This process is called "breathing" and is what keeps a human being alive. Inside the mouth there is a "tongue" and in most humans, "teeth", which are used in the human activities of speech and eating food, which I will explain about below.

On the top of the head grows a long thin substance called "hair", which can be different colours such as brown, orange, white or grey. Some Humans cut their hair to keep it short, whilst others let it grow long. In the male humans, hair also grows around the mouth area and on the chin. If they do not cut it back, it will form a "moustache" above the mouth and a "beard" below the mouth and round its sides. It is this face area which makes each human being look different to other human beings.

Finally, inside this head part is the "skull" which contains the human centre of operations called "the brain". This is where information is taken in, processed and either stored or rejected. In short, it is the place where decisions are made about what the human being will do every moment of its life on Earth.

There is one other thing to mention. human beings have a layer of fine material which covers their body which is known as "skin". The skin colour on the humans can be all sorts of colours, though most skin colour is a different shade of brown, which can be light or dark, dependent on where those human beings first lived on Earth. In earlier times, some human beings called other humans names according to their skin shade, such as white, black, yellow or red, emphasising their difference to each other as a form of fear and ignorance. But in recent times, most human beings have stopped being concerned with the shade of skin colour that other human beings have on their bodies and now accept the other human beings as equal to them.

Human Senses

We will now look at the functioning part of the human being called "the senses".

Location - The Dordogne, France: a family having a picnic

The sun was shining high in the cloudless sky. Birds sang as they swooped from tree to tree. A family of seven was just finishing off their enjoyable picnic on a pleasant summer's day. There were two parents, a mother, and a father with their three children, as well as the maternal grandparents. The two older children were playing "catch" in a field, as they'd finished eating their picnic. The youngest child, three year old Eve, didn't want to join them. Instead, she sat there transfixed at all the sights and sounds around her. She could see the sheep grazing in a field on the hillside next to them. She watched as they chewed away at the luscious green grass, their thick woollen coats shining in the sun. She put her hand onto the soft grass beyond the rug that they were sitting on. It felt cold, yet pleasant to touch. She looked closely at it and watched a tiny ant climbing up one of the blades of grass. She was fascinated at the sight. Next, she picked up a small cake from her plate and took a bite. It tasted delicious. Finally, she looked towards her mother and father who were chatting happily away with her grandparents. She could hear what they were saying, but she didn't yet understand their grown up language. Eve also noticed the smell of tobacco smoke coming from her grandfather's pipe. She felt secure knowing that they cared for her and loved her. She was happy and contented and felt one with everything around her.

The one thing which makes the human beings unique amongst all other species in the Universe is that they have unique human "senses". These help them to understand and interact with their planet in a human way that is different from the other Earth creatures. These senses are designed to help them function properly as human beings and cope with life on Planet Earth. From the event-capture you are looking at, you should be able to identify the six main senses that human beings possess. These main senses are: - sight, smell, touch, taste, hearing and understanding. Each of these is necessary for the human body to work to its full potential. Virtually all human beings have these senses, but occasionally there are some human beings who do not possess all of these senses.

Let me explain about the senses.

"Sight" is the first sense and this is where the eyes come into use, as they tell the human what is there to be seen on Earth. The signals which the eyes send to the brain help the human being to observe all that is going on around them. The sense of sight can help the human to see all sorts of information displayed in front of them. In some cases, the sense of sight can help the human being to escape from a dangerous situation. In other cases, the human will observe the various workings of the planet or other humans and react to what he or she sees.

The next sense, "smell", is concerned with the workings of the nose which can detect thousands of different smells that occur on Planet Earth. I know it is difficult for you to comprehend this concept, but it is like energy given out from other living things on the Earth, indicating its unique vibration.

Closely connected to the sense of smell is the sense of "taste", the two of which, work in harmony with each other. Taste occurs in the mouth region and especially on the tongue. It is an indicator to the brain of whether a substance that goes into the body is safe or dangerous and can be either unpleasant or pleasurable to the human body.

The next sense is "hearing", where vibrations from other creatures are taken into the human body in the form of sound waves. Again, you may find this difficult to understand, but planet earth is one planet where sound is important and so varied that I will go into more detail about this later on.

"Touch" is the sense that is associated with the hands and in particular the fingers of the hands. Signals are sent to the brain from the finger tips telling it what the substance or material the human being is touching feels like. Touch can tell a human how hot or cold a substance is, whether it is vibrating with life or not, and whether it feels pleasant to the touch or not. It is not just the fingers that are capable of the sense of touch though. These are the main gateway for touch signals to the brain, but the whole of the body is designed to use the sense of touch through that layer I mentioned earlier called skin.

Finally, there is one more sense which I have called "understanding", though the humans can call it by different names such as "Intuition" or "consciousness". Basically, this sixth sense is based in the brain of the human body and is a tool which speaks to the human being about what the other five senses are telling the human body. It can warn the human being of danger, of pleasure, of pain and it is this that guides the human on its life journey.

Now that you have learnt about the human senses, you might be surprised to know that the human body is not a continuous vessel of energy. Rather it needs to take in different energy forms to maintain its movement. Then, every so often it will also stop moving and rest to renew its internal energy, unlike us who move and exist constantly. Let me show you what human beings need to do to receive their energy.

Human Energy needs

Now that you understand how the human body works and functions, I will briefly mention about where it gets its energy from to grow and move about.

On Planet Earth there are two basic energy forms the human beings and animals need to exist. These are called "air" and "water". The air energy is there in the atmosphere all around them and moves in and out of human beings and animals in the breathing process. This is the basic life process on Earth and without it the human beings and animals would cease to continue or "die" as they call it.

The other thing they need to survive is water, which like air moves into and out of the human body. The water comes in through the mouth at the front of the human body and this is called "drinking". It then passes through the body and is expelled though another opening lower down the body when it has done its job. In fact, most of the human body is made up of water, apart from the flesh and bones which hold it together. Human beings can live without water for much longer than without air, but if they don't take in enough of these two ingredients eventually the human body will stop working.

The Energy Source of Food

There is one more thing that virtually every human being takes into their body to give them growth and strength and that is the energy form called "food". You may find it strange that human beings do this, as on our planet we have no such need for energy in the form of food, yet this is a part of human existence on Earth.

Let us now have a look at the two main sources of food that can be found on Planet Earth.....

Food from plants

The first food source for human beings is the source that comes out of the ground in the form of fruit and vegetables. Apart from the humans, there are lots of different life forms on Planet Earth including animals, birds and fishes, which all move about the Earth. Then there is another group called "plants", which includes trees and grasses which stay rooted to the ground in one place. These plants take in their food energy from the "Sun", which Planet Earth is orbiting. It is the Sun's light energy which inhabits these plants, along with water from above the ground and the nutrients and water moisture from inside the ground. Their basic colour is green which is indicative of the chlorophyll inside them. They start off as a "seed" and expand into a flower, bush or tree, which all produce different coloured "buds" which are there to attract the birds and the bees to transfer their pollen. Let us look at this in action on Earth.

Location - North East England: an allotment plot

The seventy five year old man sat down on the chair which he had taken out of the shed and looked at his allotment. He had rented it from the local council for the past thirty years and had grown countless crops of fruit and vegetables on it during that time, It was now August and the sight before him was a mixture of various shades of green, interspersed with reds, whites and yellows, as all that hard work of the past few months was coming to fruition.

It had been a good year for his allotment. As usual the Earth had produced far more than he and his wife needed. There were potatoes, peas, runner beans, parsnips, carrots, lettuces and cucumbers. A month earlier he had harvested a bumper crop of raspberries and strawberries, not to mention blackcurrants and gooseberries. Behind him, his prize racing pigeons cooed in their ramshackle wooden coup.

The old man sat there observing the scene before him as well as listening to the sounds around him. He was contented with life: - no job to have to make him get up early every day; plenty of food on the table: a loving wife and family. "What more could a man want in life?" he thought. Very soon his two grandchildren would come through the gate at the end of the allotment and greet him with the words, "What can we pick from your allotment today Grandpa?"

This event-capture shows you the food source from plants growing in the ground and up from it. Within this group you get fruit and vegetables and cereals which also grow out of the ground. The fruit is the seeds which grow out of the buds on the end of the fruit bushes and trees. They have different names and colours such as "raspberries", "oranges", "plums", "pears" and "apples". Many aeons ago the humans discovered that they could eat these fruits straight from the plants and get energy from them.

The vegetables which the humans eat also grow from out of the ground and in most cases are from smaller plants than the fruit plants. Most vegetables actually grow under the ground such as "potatoes", "carrots" and "beetroot". But there are some vegetables that do grow above ground such as "beans", "peas", "broccoli", and "sprouts". Again, the humans have discovered that these plants are safe to eat and have used them as a food source energy ever since. There are other plants and fruits that the humans can't eat as these would kill them. They eventually learnt that if you heated these vegetables in water you could get a different taste from them, which was quite pleasant!

Cultivation

In the early days of human existence on Planet Earth it seems that the humans just picked what food they wanted from the trees or bushes or pulled plants up from out of the ground. They called this "foraging" and many human beings still practise this method of searching for food in some parts of the planet, just as many animals do. But gradually some human beings learnt about the life processes of these foods including the processes of "germination" and "fertilisation" and developed the practice of "cultivation" of plants and grasses.

This meant that they were able to grow these plants in special areas of the planet that they had set aside for them. For instance, they could grow a lot of potatoes in one area, or a lot of strawberries in another – just as the old man has done in his allotment garden in the event-capture I have shown you. In fact, the cultivation of grasses led to these types of plants becoming one of the primary food energy sources for human beings around the Earth. They learnt that certain grasses gave off cereal foods such as wheat, oats, barley and rice; and these became a major source of food energy intake for them. They also found that the hard fruit of some trees, which they called "nuts", was also another energy food source for their bodies.

But for many Human Beings this food energy source is not the only one they have. Let me show you another one.

Food from animals

Location - Dublin, Ireland: a meat processing factory *

Billy pushed aside the thick, long plastic sheets that hung over the entrance to the slaughterhouse. He clocked in and went to his locker, where he proceeded to change into his once white, but now blood-stained overalls. For anyone coming into that building for the first time, the stench was overwhelming. But Billy had been working here for eighteen months and was now hardened to it. Apart from the smell of death, there was the noise of the heavy machinery, which towed the carcasses of the cows along an overhead conveyor belt. His job at the moment was to cut open the carcasses and let all the insides drop onto the floor into a trough, where they would be processed and made into sausages. He preferred this job to the one he had previously in the factory, which was to use the electric gun on the cows to kill them before dispatching them for hooking up. He often thought about his job and whether he would quit it, but always he came to the same conclusion…"If I leave here, there's no other job for me and I don't want to be back on the dole. No thank you!"

From this scene you can see that the human beings have a second food energy source – that is the flesh of animals that live on the land, (as well as the fish that live in the sea). How come humans eat the flesh of the animals you may ask|?

When human beings first populated the Earth, all the animals intermingled freely with humans, without fear, trusting them implicitly. They were friends with each other. Human beings would only eat the vegetation that grew out of the Earth, just as the animals did, as there was more than enough of this energy source. In fact, there was no fear between human beings and the animals and this stayed this way until an event called "The Change" happened. The Change was a process whereby human beings changed from living in harmony and peace with each other and with the animals and with the Earth, to living apart from them.

Instead, from that time onwards human beings started to live separately from each other and from the animals. They started to become violent to each other and to the animals. In fact, they began an action known as "killing". This means stopping another creature from continuing its life existence on Earth. Human beings started to kill the animals and the animals even started killing each other. Not only did human beings just kill the animals, but they also started to eat the flesh of the animals which they called "meat". Also, the larger animals started to kill and eat the smaller animals too, until what the human beings call, a "food chain" developed. This practice continues to this day. There are, however, some human beings who just eat the food that grows out of the ground and they deliberately do not eat animals. They are called "Vegetarians", or "Vegans" if they do not eat animal products either.

Not only do many of the human beings kill the animals to eat them as food, but they also kill them for their products like their skin, or body hair or inside parts. Human beings have become so sophisticated at killing animals that there they are several types which have become especially favoured by the humans to eat. These include cattle, sheep, pigs and chickens. There are also certain human groups on Earth that eat other less popular animals for food like horses, dogs, snakes, rats and insects. The first group of animals have become so popular as human food, that they are now specially bred for that purpose in custom built buildings as you have just seen in the event-capture. Their sole existence as animals on Earth is to be killed and eaten as human food. The humans also eat fish and other sea creatures that live in the water that cover the planet. These also are killed and then eaten either raw or cooked by many human beings.

As you can see from the last event-capture I have just shown you, the human beings have built special factories for killing the animals and processing their body parts. Not many human beings are able to work in a place like this however, as the smell of death is so overpowering. The food parts that come from the animals that are killed is called "meat" but is not eaten raw by the human beings, as the other animals do. Instead, it is heated or "cooked" so that it changes colour and texture and is thus more appealing to the humans, who then devour it in great quantities as you will see in the scene below.

Food Excess

As I have said earlier, Planet Earth was designed by The Source so that there would never be a shortage of anything that the human beings needed, especially in the need for food energy. Yet the desire and need by some human beings for this food energy has led to there being two sorts of human being on the Earth today – those who have more than enough food and those who do not have enough food. Let me show you how.

Location - A town in the Mid-West of the USA: the living room of a suburban house

A thirty something male was slouched across the sofa in his living room, his eyes transfixed on a ball game on his TV set. He was seriously over-weight, yet still felt the need to eat snacks when the fancy took him. He hadn't done any exercise for the past ten years, yet he seemed more concerned with whatever was on the TV, rather than with his own health.
On the small table on his left, next to the sofa, lay a half empty cup of cola which had lost its fizz. Next to it was a plate with the crusts of a bacon sandwich on it, waiting for someone to take it away. On his right on the sofa was an array of gadgets including remote controls for changing the TV stations, setting the DVD recorder, his land line phone, a cell phone and a games consol for when he got bored with whatever was on the TV.
The doorbell rang and he shouted to his wife,
"Can you get that, Honey?"
Obediently, his wife got up from her chair in the kitchen, where she was watching a soap opera on the other TV. She opened the door to the pizza delivery man, who handed over two large, short crust pizzas; one marguerite with salami and mushroom topping; the other chicken and sweet corn with

tomato. This was accompanied by a bag of fries and barbeque sauce.

She took the pizzas off him and gave him his money, before shutting the door. She went straight into the living room and gave her husband his pizza box and fries, without saying a word. She then returned to her soap opera, hoping that she hadn't missed any of the storyline. He opened his box and tore off a slice, the melted cheese clinging onto the rest of the pizza before he devoured the slice. Then he ate another one and another one.........

From this event-capture that I am showing you, it can be seen that the human beings are having difficulty making the best use of the food energy that they have. These humans have too much of it and do not use all the food that they have. They leave lots of it uneaten and it is then unused or "wasted".

Some human beings eat too much of one type of food, especially meat and not enough of other foods like vegetables and fruit. They also like to eat a lot of "processed food", which is food made in a factory where lots of ingredients are added to it, so it can be eaten a long time after it has been made. This is because natural food has a certain length of time that it will stay fresh for and then it will start to die and not be suitable as a food. If the humans eat too much of these foods which are acid based, the natural alkalis in the natural foods will be taken over by the more acidic processed foods inside their bodies. And so, this will be stored inside their bodies as fat and so their body shape will change into something much bigger than it should be. As a result of humans eating only certain foods that they are attracted to, not only do they become too big, but these foods alter their "health" or natural state of being, which I will explain about below.

In many cases, human beings begin to be unhappy about their body shape and so they start to miss out eating some foods altogether in this quest to find the right body shape. These are called "diets" and have caused untold misery to many human beings, who fail to achieve what they thought they would achieve by following this diet. In the end they become even more unhappy than the were in the first place, and then they start to eat more than they need to and become even bigger and heavier than they need to be!

Food famine

There is another side to this type of food energy though and that is the human being who is not getting enough food energy into their body. Here is an example of this in action.

Location – South Sudan, Africa: a drought stricken area *

The woman had walked seven miles in the searing heat, which was beating down mercilessly on her and her five month old baby girl, who was perched on her back. The baby was weak with malnutrition. For a second year the much-needed rains had failed to materialise and yet again the harvest had been a poor one. As there was no food left in the woman's village, she had been forced to walk twenty miles to the nearest feeding station for help.
"Please help me!" she cried out in a feeble voice to the relief worker. "My baby is dying!" The worker from the aid charity lifted the helpless baby from her back and took her straight to the medical centre. It was already full to overflowing with fourteen babies and twice as many more children in it. The two medical staff from the charity were overwhelmed with the workload that these human beings presented. The woman, exhausted after her walk, was too weak to stop her baby being taken, and stood there silently weeping. She thought of her two other children back in the village and wondered would the charity workers help her? Would they let her have food to take back to them? Would they even believe her?
After a few hours the food she had received was giving her back some strength to her brittle body. She was still too weak to walk back to her village and slept on the ground outside the medical centre. She would never leave her baby whilst it still had life in her. Time stood still as she fretted over the future of her baby. But two days later, the nurse came out of the medical centre and looked straight into her eyes.... Instinctively she knew that her baby had died.

The other type of human being that I am now showing you in this event-capture is one that does not have enough food energy for its body. This is called "starvation" as the human body is not receiving enough food energy for it to function properly. In this process the body becomes smaller and lighter than it should be. The human being finds that it does not have much energy to move about and do things as it normally does. The human grows weaker and can become "ill", which I will tell you about later in my report. In the scene I have just shown you, this is what happened to the human baby as it didn't receive enough food energy to survive. Eventually hundreds of thousands of human beings become like this and the life force leaves their human bodies much earlier than you would expect them too.

This happens mainly because there is not enough food growing out of the ground in these areas, which will feed all the human beings here. It might be because the soil has become too dry through lack of rain reaching it, or it might be that the food that is grown here is taken away to other humans in other parts of the world. Whilst there are not as many of these human beings as the first type, it seems strange that those with too much food are not sharing their food with those who don't have enough food.

Whilst there is more than enough food energy available on Earth for all human beings at the present time, it is not being shared equally, so that everybody gets their fair share. This is the first major problem I have seen on Planet Earth and it is one which the human beings are perfectly capable of solving......if they want to.

Now before I move onto the next part of my report. Let me tell you about some more basic human needs.

Sleep

The first part of this section shows us the basic human need for a thing called "sleep". Let me show you and example of this.

Location - Lima, Peru: the bedroom of a house in a shanty town

Camila was at her wits end. Her baby son had just finished feeding from the bottle and she was shattered. It had been a busy day at work yesterday and she really needed her sleep to be on top form for her job she had to go to later on that day. It was now three o'clock in the morning and she'd been awake for the past hour feeding her son, Alfredo, on and off. He was the sort of baby who would sleep for a little while and then wake up, demanding to be fed. She gently patted his back to get the excess wind out of him and waited for the burp. Nothing came, so she patted his back once more. "Please go to sleep!" she whispered. Yet he started to cry even more. Camila too started to cry. It was all too much. How was this going to end?

All humans move about to some degree, but sooner or later they have to stop moving about as the body needs to do something which is called "rest". The process starts when they don't move about as much as normal and their mouth will give them a signal when it opens wide in an action called "yawning". This is the start of a sensation called "tiredness". They find that they cannot continue moving or thinking at the speed they usually do. Instead, they feel the need to lie down horizontally and then the brain shuts down for a period and they change to a human experience called "sleep".

All human beings have to sleep at some time, as it is the way in which the human body recharges itself, ready for more activity and movement. Babies and children need more sleep than adult humans, even though at times they will fight the need to sleep, as you have just seen in the event-capture. Eventually all humans will go to sleep, as that is how the human body is designed. How long they sleep for depends on their human age and how much movement they have done that day. Generally speaking, most humans tend to sleep when the Earth is facing away from their star and there is darkness in the sky. But some humans and all babies have a need to sleep when there is light in the sky during the daytime.

Human injury and pain

After having slept, the humans should be refreshed and ready to move about again. Sometimes however the humans stay asleep for a longer period of time than usual. This is because the body needs to rest for much longer due to the human body experiencing a human state called "healing". This is where the human body is repairing damage which has happened to it for various reasons. Let me show you an example of this.

Location - Seoul, South Korea: the playground of a primary school

The school bell rang, indicating it was playtime and the playground started to fill up with children entering it from the classrooms surrounding it. What was once silence suddenly became a loud cacophony of shouting, screaming, laughing, and singing. Some children were playing football, whilst others were skipping over a skipping rope twirling round and round. Many just huddled together in small groups chattering away.
One little girl was walking along, talking to her friend when a larger boy came chasing after a football. His eyes were only on the ball as he crashed into her, knocking her over. She went tumbling onto the playground floor, scraping her hands and right knee on the tarmac. Blood started to ooze from the cut on her knee and she started to cry. Straight away the teacher on duty ran over and picked her up, taking her into the building to the first aid room where another teacher was on hand to deal with her wound.
"Don't worry, darling", she said. "We'll soon have you right as rain!" She cleaned the wound and held a small gauze over it until the blood had stopped flowing. Then she stuck a large plaster over the cut. "There", she said. "All done!. You can go back to the playground now".

From this event-capture you can see what happens when the human body is disturbed by another energy force. You will notice that when a human body is not able to stand upright, it always moves to the ground. This is because Planet Earth has a force field that keeps all objects, whether human or animal, attached to the surface. This is called "gravity" and has a magnetic effect on the life forms that live on the Earth. Only the birds and the insects are able to move away from the Earth's surface, due to their design. All other species might try to move upwards in a motion called "jumping", but due to gravity they will always be pulled downwards back to the surface of the Earth.

This is why so many humans go through an action to their bodies which they call "injury", where the body is damaged in some way. This mainly happens to children and very old humans who are not as secure at standing upright as adult humans. As you have just seen, the force of a fall to the ground can result in the body skin being "cut" or opened up. When the skin is cut, the red liquid in the human body known as "blood" comes to the surface and will keep leaving the body unless its flow is stopped.

At the same time as an injury to the human body comes a human notion that you will find strange, as we do not experience it with our highly vibrating bodies. It is the notion of hurt within the human body and this feeling is called "pain". It is an inbuilt warning system in the human body to say that something is not working properly, or that the surface of the human body has been cut or opened in a thing known as a "wound". The instruction that goes to the human brain is that something quickly needs to be done to the human body to repair this problem, otherwise the pain will continue until the wound or problem has been sorted.

Human illness

You would think that once the human beings have been born and start eating the food energy and growing, that is all that happens to the body. Yet from my observations I have seen that this isn't always so. Many human beings of all ages seem to suffer from a condition called "illness". Let me show you this human condition.

Location - Melbourne, Australia: a hospital oncology department

"Eileen Phillips!" shouted the nurse across the waiting area of the Oncology department. She had been dreading this moment. She walked slowly through the door, swiftly followed by her husband, Alan. Sitting at the desk was a middle aged man, his hair greying, looking at a computer screen over the top of his reading glasses. He looked up. "Please sit down, Mrs. Phillips, Mr. Phillips", said Mr. Henry, the consultant.

"How are you feeling today?" he asked nonchalantly. "Eileen mumbled a short "OK" and looked down.

"Well, your biopsy results are now in, which give us a clearer picture of what's going on in your stomach". He paused. "I'm afraid it's not good news Mrs Phillips..... The results indicate that there is cancer in your stomach".

Eileen immediately felt queasy and faint. Her husband gasped her hand reassuringly. She looked up at Mr. Henry, waiting to hear what he was going to say next. At the same time a thousand thoughts were going through her head: 'Am I going to die? What will happen to the children? How will Alan cope?'

"It's not all bad news, Mrs. Phillips", continued the consultant. This type of cancer is very easy to treat using chemotherapy, or in some cases radiation treatment. Though it will mean you will feel pretty groggy for the next few months. But the cost of this is well worth you getting rid of the cancer.

She was hardly listening to what the consultant was saying as more questions clouded her brain. She did pick up on the words "Chemotherapy" and "Radiation" and felt a wave of despair flow over her.

The consultant's words, "We need to discuss your treatment options in more detail, Mrs. Phillips", distracted her from her thoughts and brought her back to her senses.

This is just one example of the human condition called "illness", where the human body seems to malfunction and not work as it should. Illness manifests itself in the body when it is not able to move as quickly as it should. Or the human body's natural temperature is much higher or lower than it should be. Or food that is taken into the body is quickly expelled the way it came in. In every case the human being suffering from illness cannot live the way it was meant to live. The humans call this having a "disease" and it is caused by the human's immune system not being able to deal with a foreign body or "germ" or "virus" which has entered the body. These germs can enter the body in such numbers that eventually the human body ceases to work completely and that human dies.

Of course, there are certain energy substances that human beings can take into their bodies to help them fight these diseases, which they call "medicines". These can be either solid or liquid and have been formed from various chemicals which were once in the ground. They have the effect of telling the human body to destroy these germs and so make them well again.

There are some humans whose sole job is to help other humans who might be ill or who have had an accident. They are known as "doctors", "nurses" and "surgeons". They work in specially designed buildings called "surgeries" or "hospitals". Though in some countries on the planet there are very few of these places. Plus, not all humans have access to these places or the medicines, or they are fearful of the effect they might have on their body. So, in some cases the humans use "natural" medicines which are grown from out of the Earth to counteract the germs. Or they use energy practises or "therapies" whereby energy is accessed from another source and passed into the body of the ill person to get rid of the disease.

What many human beings don't realise is that in the early years of human beings living on Planet Earth, human beings lived for much longer than the present seventy or eighty years they live for at present. Human beings then were what you would call, "super-healthy", with no disease or illness at all. They ate completely natural food, with no human made parts added to it. They were relaxed about their lives and didn't rush around the Earth like today's human beings. They looked after each other's needs and everyone felt part of the Whole.

At the time of my visit, it would seem that most human beings have forgotten about this ability to enjoy life on Earth as a human being, and instead spend much of their time living in fear and worrying about their lives. But you will learn more about these types of human beings later on in my report.

It is now time to conclude this section of my report, which I hope will have given you an understanding as to how the human body works. In the next part I will talk about the planet that the human beings live on and how the humans interact with it.

Part 2

Human Planet

And what's your precious life but a gift to you?
Who could have put you here in green and blue?

The human beings that you have seen so far in my report are just a micro-fraction of all the life forms that live on Planet Earth. There are so many different types of life on the planet that it would take aeons to describe them all. But for now, I will leave telling you about the humans as I want to let you know about the planet itself and how it works.

The Earth planet

The Earth planet is just one of several that orbit its star in the area of the Universe that the humans call "the Milky Way". But none of the other planets in this star system have the necessary ingredients that are needed to support human life, so this is what makes the Earth quite unique. As you know there are myriads of star systems all over the Universe, each with their own sun or star, being orbited by many planets, some of them with life forms on them, but all of them are different than those in the Earth's star system.

Earth is the densest of all the planets in its star system because it is composed of solids, of which iron is the main component. But there are also traces of sulphur, silicon, magnesium, aluminium and nickel according to my observations. These are all bound by the gas oxygen, which helps provide the Earth with its many life forms. It is these metallic substances which gives the Earth its unique magnetic gravity that attracts objects from space to its surface. It also means that objects on the surface of the Earth will usually be pulled back to the Earth's surface as the gravitational force is so strong.

Yet it is the water on Earth that dominates the lives of those creatures that live on the planet. In fact, it is the water on this planet, along with the oxygen, which has led to life being created here. The water can be observed mainly on the surface, but it can also be found underground. From out of the water came life in many different and varied forms, most of them unlike any you will find in the whole Universe.

Apart from giving life to both plants and animals, the Earth also supports many other life forms, much smaller than them. These include fungi, bacteria, archaea, and plastids, which are so small that the humans themselves cannot see them, unless they use an instrument that magnifies them to a larger size.

One important thing that you should know about is that the planet is a living structure. Although the humans live on the surface, they are subject to the actions of the planet at all times. Most of the time, this does not affect the life forms at all, but on some occasions it can affect them all in a big way. Let me show you two examples.

The Climate of Planet Earth

The waters that cover the Earth are connected to the atmosphere of the planet and play an important part in how all species survive. Let me explain.

Human beings have called this process of the way in which the water moves and reacts with the heat and light of the Sun the "climate", or in simple terms, "the weather". This is basically the interaction of their Sun's energy with the water and the air on the Earth's surface. As the Earth rotates and orbits its Sun, these forces all move over the surface of the Earth. Due to the movement of the Earth, the weather can be lots of different things on different parts of the planet. The most important of these processes is what the human beings call "the water cycle". Let me show you this in action.

Location – Mumbai, India: a slum area

The heat from the afternoon sun was still scorching hot and Rishi and his brother Ilesh were beginning to wilt in the high temperature. Then the atmosphere suddenly changed and clouds began to block out the sun. The two boys started to run as soon as they felt the first drops of rain. They had been out on the hot, noisy streets of Mumbai all day trying to beg for money from foreign tourists who were walking along the street. It had been a good day. Between them they had managed to collect just under fifteen rupees.

As soon as they got back to their tiny home in one of the many slums of Mumbai they would give it to their mother who would be able to buy some rice for their next meal. They knew that as it was Monsoon season there would soon be a deluge, so it was imperative to get back home as soon as possible. The sound of thunder could be heard above the noise of motor car horns and brakes screeching. It started to darken and then the deluge began. It was if the heavens had been opened up in one go. The rain was relentless and bounced back up from the pavements. They were getting soaked as they pushed past hundreds of other people all trying to get under cover by any means possible.

Finally, they arrived back at their tin shack home, but as soon as they got inside they could see water seeping in from a hole in the tarpaulin which was held precariously above their tiny room. It dripped onto their beds and their mother lifted the soiled sheets away. Just then a small stream made up of a mixture of rainwater, human excrement and all sorts of waste started rushing along the floor. They had no alternative but to abandon their home until the rain stopped..

In this event-capture water has been lifted up from the oceans and blown by the wind or moving air and deposited on the land. It then flows downhill in the form of rivers back to the sea. Nothing is ever wasted or unused. This water feeds the plants, animals and human beings and is necessary for life to continue on Earth. The human beings call this water in the air which falls on them from the sky, "rain". Yet it can come in other forms such as "fog" or "mist", and even "snow" - when the ground temperature is cold enough.

Sometimes you get an event called "flooding" where there is so much water coming from the sky and into the rivers that it gets trapped on the land and stays there for a short time. Sometimes it happens because the humans have interfered with the natural flow of the water over the land and built new routes for the rivers. These cannot cope with the amount of rain that comes out of the

sky and so the excess water moves over the banks and onto the land. Each time this happens, the Earth is cleaned and purified in a type of washing away of the old and the unclean.

Earthquakes, Tsunamis and Volcanoes

Location – near Osaka, Japan: a small fishing village

Mr Suki was just mooring up in the small harbour of his village. He had been up all night fishing for sardines. It had been a fruitful night's work. He started to unload his catch onto his pickup truck. It would be a short drive to the fish market where he would compete with other fishermen for the best price for his fish. As he unloaded his catch he had a sudden thought that the atmosphere seemed different. Maybe it was him feeling tired.

He started his engine and as he drove along the dockside, the eerie sound of the earthquake siren began. He had to make up his mind pretty quickly as to what he should do. Should he get out of his truck and stay where he was? Or should he drive away from the village and up into the hills in case the warning could be for a tsunami?

He chose the latter and after driving for a minute he stopped to pick up an old woman who was waving her arms frantically. "Danger! Danger!" she was shouting. He started driving once more and then the first tremor began. It was a strong one and made his heart pound faster. The old woman started to weep. He was leaving the village behind now and staring to climb. As he looked in his rear view mirror he could see a white line of surf moving rapidly in from the sea. He knew straight away that he had made the best decision. He pressed his right foot harder down on the accelerator and kept climbing. There was a family running ahead of him, but he couldn't stop as he instinctively thought only of himself and his survival.

As he drove on a second tremor occurred; this time, even stronger than the last. His passenger screamed. He looked in his mirror again and saw the tidal wave hitting the harbour wall and engulfing his boat and several others. He shuddered to think that he had been standing on the post only minutes earlier. He kept driving........

This event-capture shows us that the planet is a living planet with changes going on inside it and on its surface. In this instance an earthquake is occurring which has caused a tidal wave to rise up and move towards any land that is in its way. The water will eventually cover the low lying land and anything else in its path. That is why the human is going up to high ground to escape its effects. Sometimes a living mountain called a "volcano" will cause the same event to happen. In this case it will erupt and send out hot molten lave and ash into the sky and onto the land. Again, the sea will rise up and become much higher than it usually is. In both cases any human or animal life will have to move away from this event as soon as possible, or they will get caught up in its action and die. That is why life on Planet Earth can be hard for those who live there if they choose to live in the regions of the planet where this occurs.

Of course, there are many different regions on the planet where the humans live. Let us continue our visit to Planet Earth by looking at the main environments which exist there.

Water

The first type of environment of the planet I want to look at in more detail is the liquid that covers most of the surface of the Earth.

Location - The South Atlantic Ocean

The sea in this part of the planet was calm, with hardly a wave to be seen. Whichever way you looked there was sea, with no land in sight. High up above the water, an endless pale blue sky was punctured by the bright, yellow sun which caused a reflection on the surface of the sea. A pod of dolphins was moving across the ocean, jumping, and diving as they travelled in search of food. There must have been at least twenty of them with their silver blue colouring and their pointed noses, which cut into the water just as a knife cuts into butter. The whole surface of the water was an aquamarine colour, whilst in the distance a darker shape loomed up over the horizon. The dark shape moved closer into view. It was a huge sperm whale, the largest living mammal, which sent a fountain of seawater out of its spout and up into the air, before it dived down, deep into the sea. It continued its dive for several minutes, passing the dolphins, as well as hundreds of different coloured fishes; some blue, some orange, and some silver. It continued going down deeper than most fish would normally venture, before eventually slowing down as it reached the bottom of the ocean. All sorts of sea creatures lived down here including jellyfish, shrimps, algae and flatfish. The whale was joined by its partner and together they feasted on the innumerable tiny plankton which lived in this part of the ocean. This was one place on Planet Earth where the whales knew they would be safe from the human beings who had yet to venture this far down into the water.

With this event-capture, you can observe that water seems to be everywhere on the planet. You would think that water is all you find on the surface of the Earth, yet that is not so. The water actually covers just over two thirds of the surface of the planet, around twice as much as the surface land. Yet this is kept in place between the land masses of the Earth by the solid rock under the oceans and the surface land, which forms the majority of the planet. So, the water isn't as widespread on the Earth as you think it is. It just looks that way.

In the water you get life forms which are designed to live inside the water, so if they were put upon the land, they would stop living. The most numerous of these sea creatures are the "fishes", which live in all types of water, including the fresh water of the rivers which flow over the land, as well as the salt water of the seas. They come in many different colours, ranging from red and blue, through to bright yellow and green. Yet virtually all the fishes on Earth have the same basic shape of a body, with two fins and a tail protruding from them. Bigger than the fish yet having a similar body shape are the dolphins which you have just seen. There are other similar large sea creatures, such as seals, walruses, and sharks, who all feed on the fishes in the oceans. But by far the biggest type of sea creature is the whale, which you have just observed. Although whales are fish-like, they are actually mammals and breathe in air like the other mammals that live on the land. They are the biggest of all the creatures on the Earth, yet they feed off some of the smallest creatures to get the energy they need to live!

Apart from these sea creatures, there are plenty of other creatures living in the sea, such as sea horses, turtles, and shrimps to name just a few of them – all of them different than the fishes, yet still living in the water environment. Amongst the rocks on the sea bed, you will see shell creatures like crabs, cockles, coral and oysters, who all live in this water based environment. Finally, there are the sea plants which live at the bottom of the sea including sea grasses and seaweeds. The inside of the seas are virtually free from the influence of the humans in many areas, though as we shall see later in my report, human beings have still managed to affect the seas and the creatures that live in them.

Ice

Before we move on to look at the land surface of the Earth, there is a section of the planet, which is neither land nor sea, yet it is as solid as the land. This is where the water has become so cold that it has turned into a thing called "ice" which is solid, but not actually land. Let me show you an example:-

Location - The Arctic ice shelf: a polar bear looking for food

The mother polar bear knew it was time to leave her young cubs – one male, one female - and begin her search for food. All around her was white – pure white ice which was almost blinding to look at until your eyes got used to it. In the distance you could make out a feint splash of blue grey as the Arctic Ocean touched the ice shelf. But at this place large slabs of ice were dropping off the ice shelf and into the ocean in ever increasing numbers. A group of walruses were lying down on the ice, resting after feeding off the many fish that could be found in this part of the Arctic .
The polar bear meanwhile had begun her search for the necessary food in one of the most hostile environments on Planet Earth. She jumped over a crack in the ice, an inner voice reminding her of the dangers of staying too close to the sea where an ice flow could start its journey to nothingness at any instant. High above her an albatross flew north on a similar mission. It had the advantage of height and its wings. It would only be a matter of time before it would find the necessary food. It was not the same for the polar bear however, as food had become increasingly scarce for land animals in the past twenty years as the ice shelf continued to melt. A mother's instinct drove her on........

In this event-capture you can see ice which is found on the top of the Earth and on the bottom of the Earth in the places known as the "poles". The ice in the South Pole area covers mostly land underneath it, whilst the ice in the North Pole area covers mostly water. Some visitors to Earth think that this is clouds when you look at the Earth from space, but it is only when you get near the surface of the Earth that you see it is a different substance.

In most cases, the nearer the surface of the Earth is to its Sun, the warmer it is. The further the surface of the Earth is from the Sun, the colder it is. This is why when you look at the two poles of the Earth from space there is a large amount of white there. This is snow and ice which has been there for thousands of years as the ground temperature here makes the water turn into snow and ice. So, the human beings and the animals are able to experience the sensations of hot and cold, wherever they are on Planet Earth - a concept that you might find strange, as we have a constant, steady temperature on our planet.

The ice covers the two poles as that is where the sun's rays are weakest and so the ground temperature is cold enough for the water moisture here to freeze. When I say "freeze", this is the point in Earth terms where the water moisture changes from liquid vapour into solid ice. In the Ice areas there seems to be very little human or animal life, mainly because it is so cold in human terms. This means that no trees grow in these regions and very few plants can survive in these temperatures. If there is water it freezes and so no growth can take place. Also, there are virtually no places where the animals and humans can find shelter from the cold temperatures.

The only way to survive the cold is to keep the body temperature high enough, so that it does not freeze. The animals that do live in these parts have adapted themselves to suit the cold conditions. For instance, the polar bears as you have just seen, have grown very long furry coats which keep the flesh inside them warm. Also, the colour of their fur is white – almost the same as the snow and ice here, so that it can make it hard for them to be seen by the humans who might want to attack and kill them.

If you ever visit this inhospitable part of the Earth you will find that it is light all the time. This is because the Earth's star is always shining in these areas and as the Earth rotates, it always receives the sun's rays on it. The reason the Sun gives out light to the Earth is so that human beings and animals can see what there is on the Earth. This is known as "day" in human language and is when one side of the Earth is facing the Sun. When the Earth rotates away from the Sun's rays shining onto the Earth, there is darkness, which is a period in human time called "night". Here half of the Earth is not reached by the Sun's rays and it gives the Earth species a chance to rest and refresh themselves, ready for the next day's events. Humans have come to call these changes in light and darkness as their concept called "Time". I will tell you more about this human idea later on in my report.

Before we leave this region and move to look at other areas of the Earth, there is one problem which I noticed with this part of the Earth – the ice seems to be melting. It seems that the normal temperature here is being raised by warmer temperatures coming from elsewhere on the Earth. All this ice melting is not good for the ecosystem of the planet and will mean that the oceans will have more water in them than they were designed for and the eco-balance will be affected. This has been caused by the actions of human beings, who don't understand the consequences of what they are doing. I will explain more about this at the end of my report.

If we move away from the Arctic area and move further south, you can see that vegetation starts to appear as the temperature gets warmer. Generally speaking the further south you go from the top of the Earth, the hotter it becomes. This means that the conditions are better suited for both animals and plants to survive on the surface of the Earth. There are different types of vegetation though in different areas of the land surface of the Earth as we shall see.

Land

The next few event-captures that I have sent back to you come from the land surface of the Earth, as that is where the human beings and most animals exist. The land or earth provides life to thousands and thousands of life forms. They all co-exist with each other and interact with each other, giving out their energy to each other to help them all grow and develop.

The first land area I am showing you is roughly midway between the top of the Earth and the middle of it.

Location – The Highlands of Scotland: by the side of a loch

The mist was starting to lift from the loch as the sun rose higher in the sky. The mountains that surrounded the loch started to glisten as the sun's rays shone on their snow-capped peaks. Below the snow line there was a green and yellow section of bracken, interspersed with purple heather plants, swaying in the gentle breeze. Below them the sun's rays penetrated the dark green pine forests lower down the slopes. The trees covered a vast area and reached down to the water's edge on the far side of the loch. A river was flowing out of the western end of the loch over some boulders which created a swirling, white current.

Deep inside the loch, salmon were preparing to make their long journey back to the Atlantic Ocean in an annual journey that had started thousands of years ago for this species. They would swim into the river which drained out of the loch all the way to the North Atlantic Ocean. High on the slopes of the mountain where the forest trees had not yet reached, a male deer stood motionless, His canopy of antlers marking it out on the skyline. In the sky hundreds of feet above him, a golden eagle soared, surveying the region below it, able to spy out a tiny mouse or vole from hundreds of feet away.

In a field by the near edge of the loch, brown, shaggy Highland cattle were grazing on the green grass, punctuated with white daisies and other wild flowers, unaware of the wild rabbits and stoats scurrying near the grey stone walls. The breathtaking scenery here hadn't changed for thousands of years. Life was teeming everywhere from the many types of fish and freshwater creatures inside the loch, through to the different wild animals such as pine marten, red squirrels and wild cats that lived amongst the trees. In the air, mosquitoes, flies, and midges all moved freely in and out of the trees and above the water.

Although it was never that hot in this part of Scotland, life continued at a slow and relaxing pace for the locals, who were easily outnumbered by the wildlife. It was hard to imagine that less than an hour's drive from this spot lived hundreds of thousands of people. Yet that world seemed a million miles away.

We are looking here at a piece of land which is mainly green in colour, with all sorts of species living amongst it. The green indicates that life is thriving here. To begin with there are lots of trees which provide habitats for several creatures, including wild cats, squirrels, insects, and various birds. If you were expecting to see a human being here, you would be very lucky, as this part of the Earth has not been settled by human beings in large quantities, mainly because it does not have the right conditions for humans to flourish. Animals on the other hand do thrive here as there is a plentiful supply of food and water for them.

The water you can see is a lake or "loch" and is not the same as the water that you get in the seas. It is fresh water and contains no salt, yet it will eventually go back to the sea in the form of a river which flows downwards from the high ground. In this area can be found all sorts of insects, which like the birds, also fly, but they are much smaller and lighter.

There are some other animals that don't live on the surface of the Earth but move about in the space above the land. These are called "birds" and they have wings made up of feathers which help them "fly" as the humans call it. They are able to escape upwards from the Earth's gravity field because they are light enough to do so. Though there are limits as to how high up they can fly. There are also some even smaller creatures called "insects", many of which can also fly, such as bees, dragonflies, mosquitoes, and butterflies. These are lighter than the birds and tend to stay nearer the Earth's surface than the birds. The insects that don't fly, such as ants, beetles and earwigs, crawl along the ground or up the sides of flowers and trees. They all tend to make their homes in the trees and bushes and flowers that grow out of the Earth.

Vegetation

Let me tell you about the trees and flowers, as they all work in harmony with the insects and birds to help the different types of life forms to flourish on the Earth.

Location – Brazil: an equatorial rain forest in the Amazon basin

The rain had stopped pouring its contents out of the sky onto the Earth, whilst the clouds had moved away towards the sea. Steam was rising off the wide Amazon river as the sun started to shine once more. Its rays began to penetrate into the darkest recesses of the forest once more. The wide variety of trees here opened the pores of their leaves to let in the sunlight and start to grow again. All sorts of strange sounds were emanating from the trees and the forest floor. Monkeys were chattering and jumping from branch to branch. Exotic coloured birds were cawing out their mating call and flying up over the vast green canopy. Down at ground level a variety of animal life was carrying on as it had done for thousands of years on Planet Earth. There were ants marching over the tree roots, snakes slithering amongst the fallen leaves, yellow coloured frogs jumping through the undergrowth and tiny mice climbing up the tree trunks in search of food.

All of a sudden, the forest became silent. The monkeys stopped chattering, the ants stopped marching, the frogs stopped jumping and the snakes stopped slithering. The mice scurried down the tree trunks and burrowed into the undergrowth. The sound of a chainsaw roared a warning call of danger to all the inhabitants of the forest. Then there was silence. This lasted for just a few seconds. Then a creaking sound started, followed by a loud thud as another precious tree had been felled. Human beings were here....

The trees cover many different areas of the Earth in large groups called "forests". They can be found in hot or cold regions, so long as there is water and sunlight. Part of their function is to take in the gas called carbon dioxide that the humans and animals breathe out from their bodies. At the same time the trees give out oxygen through their extremities or "leaves" which cover them. The humans and animals can then breathe in the oxygen in order to survive. This helps keep the right balance of gases on the planet for the different life forms to exist. The flowers on the other hand work in harmony with the bees and the birds by providing pollen which is needed for their continued existence on Earth. The birds and the bees carry this pollen to other parts of the ground, so that the flowers and grasses will grow to provide food for the humans and animals to eat.

In this part of the planet very few humans live here as the forest is a dense barrier to human penetration. There are some humans who live here in small groups called "tribes", but they live very different lives to the rest of the humans. They are closer to the natural world and know how to survive in the forest or "jungle" as it also called. They have lived here for thousands of years. However, in the recent past these tribes and all the creatures who live here are starting to lose their homes as other humans move in to chop the trees down as the event-capture shows. I will explain more about what is happening here at the end of my report.

Now let us move down the surface of the Earth to a place which is near the middle part of the planet, which is the part nearest to the sun and so much hotter than most of the rest of the planet.

Animal Life Forms

Location - Tanzania, East Africa: the Serengeti Plain

The lioness yawned and stretched out below the Acacia tree as she watched her three young cubs playing together in the long brown grass. Overhead two vultures were looking down for any scraps that the other animals may have left them. About fifty yards to the left several elephants were drinking and washing themselves in the shallows of the river, a tributary of the Masa, which was almost full after the rains of the previous week. Water buffalo and hippos were swimming in the deeper parts and on the opposite bank beyond hundreds of marabou stork, a pack of hyenas were all drinking furiously from the fresh waters of the river.

The lioness sat up and flicked her ears back to remove the flies that rested on her. She had heard something. About a mile away clouds of dust could be seen rising up as a feint sound started to get louder. Then a whole group of around five thousand wildebeest came into view. They were on their

annual migration and soon they would envelope the whole area, only slowing to cross the river. Anything that stood in their way would be advised to give them a wide berth.
Sensing that a meal was on the cards, the lioness crept into the grass and made her way to where the passing train of wildebeest was heading. She waited for her chance and soon it came in the form of a young calf that had somehow got separated from the rest of the group. It was still running but was easily within the lioness's range. She pounced and instinctively went for its neck, killing it in seconds. It went limp and within two minutes she and her cubs were feasting on its carcass. The vultures flew closer, waiting for their chance, once the lions had finished.

In this event-capture you can see that once again there are large numbers of animals living in this part of the Earth. They are much bigger and stronger than the animals in the previous location and yet again the humans do not live in large numbers in this area, mainly because the animals are not afraid of the humans. They are what humans call "wild animals" because they live free of human control, unlike some other animals which have become "tame". The animals here have learnt to respect each other and give each other their own space, as they live on their own piece of the Earth – for most of the time.

It is now time to tell you more about the animals. Most animals that move on the surface of the Earth have four legs, such as the lion, the elephant or the wildebeest that you have just observed. The most common four legged animals on Earth are dogs, cats, horses, sheep and cattle, all of which have become tamed from their natural wild state by the humans. These all live in harmony with and in service to the human beings. But there are hundreds more animals which live naturally away from the human beings, such as lions, rabbits, badgers and deer.

There are some, like the monkeys and apes that have two legs and tend to walk upright rather than on all fours. Some animals, like snakes and worms do not have any legs at all, yet they move themselves by pulling and pushing their bodies along the ground – all quite strange to you who move instantly from place to place on our planet, just by a thought.

Some animals get their food energy by eating the plants, grasses and flowers that grow up from out of the ground. These are called "herbivores". Other animals will eat the bodies of animals that they have killed such as the lions eating the wildebeest. These are called "carnivores". Sometimes you get animals that eat both plant forms and animals and these are called "omnivores". Most human beings come into this category, but in the end all bodies break down and return to the Earth.

Deserts

So, from these different scenes that I have shown you, you can see that there is plenty of the Earth to see and experience without any human beings around. However, let me take you to an area of the Earth where human activity has resulted in the destruction of many life forms that once lived there. The humans call it "desert".

Location – Mongolia: the Gobi Desert

The yellow and black scorpion scurried between the rocks over the hot sand. It was searching for its prey - the sand lizard who was hoping to out manoeuvre him today. The temperature had reached 40 degrees Fahrenheit as the sun beat down on the desert floor. This ritual had gone on for the past thirteen years, when the last rains had fallen here. Surprisingly the desert had sprung to life at this major event with worms and flies all surfacing from deep under the sand, only to submerge again as the water evaporated back into the atmosphere. It was hard to believe that thousands of years earlier, this place had been a green jungle, gleaming with both plant and animal life, but a mixture of deforestation, over-grazing and lack of rainfall had gradually removed virtually all the life from it and the soil could longer sustain the life that it once had. Eventually the soil had turned into a golden dust, stretching for hundreds of miles in all directions. Life was still here though, albeit in tiny numbers, scratching out an existence under the sand dunes and beneath the bushes that still survived in this dry region of Earth.

This area of the Earth's surface looks completely orangey brown in colour, not too dissimilar to that of the planet next to Earth, which the humans call "Mars". This is because the land here is devoid of vegetation and life. There are several areas like this on the land surface which have the same characteristics. These areas have sand rather than soil on the surface, with no water or rain found here. It is always very hot during the day and there is hardly any animal life.

You may find this hard to believe, but these areas were once full of life and vegetation just like the two previous locations, yet the human beings in the past over-exploited the land and this killed off the life that flourished in the soil here. They cut down the trees and all the plants and eventually the soil blew away or died and turned into sand. Now these areas will never return to the way they were as the damage that has been done is irreversible. There are however small pockets of life in them where vegetation still grows. This type of place is called an "oasis" and is a place where animals and humans travelling across these deserts are able to find water and food as they were untouched by the destruction that took place aeons ago.

It would seem that whilst most of the land surface on Planet Earth is capable of supporting life, there are a few areas like the one above where life is not possible, after the humans have interfered too much with the natural order of things. This results in future generations of humans not being able to benefit from what their ancestors have done.

Now that you have seen what lies on the surface of Planet Earth, it is time to learn about how the humans interact with the Planet and how they live there.

Human Dwellings

Virtually every human being has a need for a thing which they call "shelter". There are very few humans who live outside under the stars and the Sun just as the animals and birds do. A long time ago the humans decided that they needed to find somewhere where they could rest and sleep, which was out of range of the sun's rays and away from the winds that blow over the Earth's surface, and where the water falling out of the sky couldn't touch them. At first they stayed under trees or bushes but they came to realize that they weren't the best of shelters. Other humans chose to find their shelter inside holes in the rocks which they called "caves". But eventually some humans started to create their own shelters for living in which are known as "dwellings".

At first they were made of wood and leaves from the trees that covered the land, but then one human being learnt to use the hard earth or stone from the land. They even discovered how to make their own stones which they called "bricks". They stuck these bricks together with an adhesive called "mortar" which developed into "cement" – all of them coming from out of the Earth. Gradually their dwellings or "homes" as they called them got bigger and bigger. So big in fact that many of the human beings could live inside them.

These dwellings were different shapes and sizes according to their skills and needs. But soon it came to pass that most humans chose to build their dwellings inside in a box like structure which became more complicated and intricate over human time. They came to be built out of wood, plaster and bricks, as you will see in the event-capture below.

Houses

Location - Calgary, Canada: a house under construction

The foreman at the building site was getting angry and frustrated. He was in charge of a new build of two detached houses and the five men under him were sitting around doing nothing.

"Look!" he shouted down his mobile phone. "You promised me that my order of the bricks and cement would be here on site by 4 o'clock yesterday. It's now 10 o'clock in the morning and they still haven't arrived!" The voice at the other end in the Builder's Merchants was trembling with fear. "I'm really

sorry about that, Sir. I'll just check on our screen and see what's happened".
The foreman sighed and looked around him. The footings had been dug and the foundations laid. The drains were sorted last week. Now all he needed was the bricks to start building upwards. He needed the brickies to press on as he had the electricians and plumbers booked in for next week. If the walls and floors weren't done, then that would be even more costly and more delays meant money would be lost.

From the event-capture here you can see a human home being built by other humans. You and I see it as a box as that is a shape we are familiar with on our planet. Yet the humans have given these boxes various names such as "house", "flat", "bungalow" or "maisonette". The humans have come to spend a lot of their lives inside these boxes which can vary in size and shape. As they construct these boxes they attach various objects and power sources to them to serve their human needs. Usually there are several of the boxes placed together for the humans to spend their time in. Over the ages the humans have placed more and more of these boxes by the side of existing boxes, or even on top of each other, so that whole communities of humans living together in one place have come into existence.

A small number of these boxes together is called a "village", whilst a large number is called a "town" or a "city". Some of this latter group are now so big that millions of the humans are crammed together with very little heat and light in them. The result is that the humans do not get much sleep because of the constant noise coming out of these structures. They also get angry and fight with each other in these places, and human illnesses and diseases thrive within them. You will know that you have reached a city or a town when you visit the planet by the large amount of these boxes or buildings crammed together, and by the lack of green vegetation.

Some humans have also built barriers around their homes and put this extra space to other uses. Some grow the food energy of fruit and vegetables on this area of land, whilst others just let it become green in colour and then they sit down on it or run about on it. Other humans dig a big hole in this space and then fill the hole with water. They then jump into this water and move about in it as it gives them great pleasure. If you want to find humans on Earth, just look out for these boxes on the land surface.

There are a few humans on the planet who have managed to persuade other humans to build them lots of boxes together. They are so big that you can easily see them from a long way in the distance. They don't need all these rooms, but because they are powerful humans, they feel the need inside themselves to show their power by having a much bigger home than most of the rest of the humans. Inside these homes they have put in lots of intricate artwork and pictures and objects as signs of their power. They call these homes their "palace" or "mansion".

Yet there are still more human boxes which are not used as homes by the humans. Instead, these constructions have many uses and I will show you some of the more important ones now.

Human Buildings

Apart from the dwellings that the humans call "homes" there are many other structures that the humans have built during their time on Planet Earth which they call "buildings". These are used by humans for all sorts of purposes apart from living and sleeping in. Let me show you an example.

Location - Cairo, Egypt - the Great Pyramid of Giza

It was already well into the eighties as the sun shone out across the desert towards the three large pyramids, and the Sphinx on the Giza Plateau. Beyond them the noise and smells of Cairo were emanating outwards. In the distance on the other side of the pyramids three tourists were riding on camels, led by a single Egyptian guide. They were living the tourist dream of riding a camel in the shadow of the pyramids. In front of the largest pyramid, a group of about twenty tourists were listening to a local guide telling them about the history of the pyramid known as Cheops Pyramid. They were a mixture of Americans, Europeans and Japanese who eagerly listened to all that the guide was telling them.

"When the Pharaoh was buried here the pyramid that you now see, had taken over twenty years to build, with thousands of slaves press-ganged into its construction. Each stone that was used in the pyramid weighs 30 tonnes and was dragged from the quarry over there onto a specially built slope". She waved her left arm towards the quarry area, making sure the tourists were paying attention.

"The stones that you see above were then put on logs and rolled up the slope , being pulled by slaves before being wedged into place. No wonder it took so many years to build the pyramid!! She paused for effect and then continued.

"Inside the pyramid, secret walkways were built into the stones for the priests to get to the King's and Queen's chambers. We will shortly be going down the main one into the King's Chamber. Before we do so, are there any questions?"

From this event-capture you can see some humans visiting an ancient building which was built not for a human to live in, but as a human tomb. For many years this was the tallest building in the world before other taller buildings were built. They constructed large buildings like this for a variety of reasons, but mainly to show the power and status of certain humans. To do this they needed lots of other humans to build them and so many humans were forced to help build these sort of places. Later, in human history many buildings were built as places for the humans to work in, or for humans to rule over a certain area of land.

One such type of building was known as a "castle". This was because there came a time when human beings no longer lived equally and in harmony with each other and so they started to change the building of their homes they lived in. They were afraid that other human beings might come and attack them, so they started to build homes that could stop other human beings from attacking and destroying them. These buildings were so large that a large number of humans lived in them at the same time.

Basically, these castles were built for protection, but they also built equally large buildings where they could communicate with The Source according to their belief systems. These buildings were decorated with coloured glass and were taller in many cases than the castles, yet the human beings didn't actually live in them. Instead, the Human beings were only allowed inside them on certain days and at certain times of the week. They had the names of cathedrals, temples and mosques. These were buildings designed for religious practices which I will come to later on in this report.

Now there are millions of buildings all over the planet with names such as "offices", "headquarters", "town halls" and "hotels". These are found mainly in the middle of a settlement and are crowded together, with the humans' houses all around them. You will find out more about these places later in my report.

Next I will tell you about how the humans move around their planet.

Part 3

Human Movement

Moving down an open road,
With an element of speed,
Feeling good to be alive....

It is now time to learn about how the humans interact with each other, as human beings are constantly moving about, either in their bodies, or in special containers which they have created to transport them all over the Earth. Let us start by looking at basic human movement.

Walking and running

Location - Athens, Greece: the final stages of a marathon race

The crowds lining the streets started cheering and clapping as the lead runners came into view. There was a single Ethiopian runner leading, but a few metres behind a group of four runners were trying desperately to catch him. Behind them hundreds more were pushing their bodies to the limit, which were constantly dehydrating in the intense Greek heat. The runners had left the town of Marathon just over two hours ago, following a course which climbed upwards on occasion and descended steeply at other times. Eventually they reached the suburbs of Athens. Now, the Parthenon's distinctive outline could be seen clearly ahead up on top of the Acropolis Hill which dominated this part of Athens.
They seemed to be moving in slow motion if you watched them coming towards you, legs and arms moving in unison, feet pounding on the grey tarmac. In just a few minutes a huge cheer would echo around Athens as the first runners would

enter the stadium and the Marathon race would reach its climax.

The human body is designed in such a way that its limbs and everything connected with it are programmed for movement. As I have told you, the humans are different from virtually every other animal on the planet in that they stand upright on two legs, rather than stay bent over on four legs. Their legs rest upon the feet, which they sometimes cover with containers which they call "shoes". These are designed to protect the feet from the hard and sharp surfaces on the ground.

You might find this concept of movement difficult to understand as we don't move in the slow human sense, but just think ourselves as being in a particular place and we are instantly there. Yet the humans move around by moving their two legs at varying speeds – all very slow and tedious by our standards.

The most common movement of humans is called "walking" when they move their feet and legs forwards at a steady speed. Sometimes their legs move forwards much quicker than with walking, moving to their peak limit and this is called "running", when the speed of movement is increased. All these movements are co-ordinated by the brain which utilises the human body's muscles, eyes, heart, and lungs to make this movement happen. This is what you are observing in the event-capture. This then is the basic form of human movement and is used by all humans who are able to use this method of movement. I would add that humans can also move upwards and downwards, such as walking up a mountain side, or crawling downwards into a hole in the ground.

You will have noticed that human babies don't move about like adults or even child humans. This is because this walking movement has yet to be learnt by such young humans. It has to be learnt and developed within every human being. At first human babies hardly move at all, as they rely on their mothers and other adult human beings to feed them and nurture them. Eventually they start to move using their arms to pull the rest of the body forward. This is called "crawling" and this eventually develops into "standing", when the baby can rest its whole body on its feet. Then gradually it will start to move its legs forwards taking its first tentative steps as it learns to walk. Of course, there are many times when the baby will fall over, as it tries to master this basic of human movement. But once it has overcome this challenge, it will soon start to walk by itself, though it will need close supervision to make sure it doesn't go where it could hurt itself.

Skiing and skating

Location – Switzerland: a ski resort in the Alps

Jan picked up his skis from the rack by the front door of his hotel and walked out gingerly onto the snow. He was 10,000 feet up at a resort in the Swiss Alps. Surrounding the small village were majestic mountains whichever way he looked. The sun was shining down upon him, so him put his ski goggles on and then bent down to put his skis on. He then stood back up and looked all around him.
"I think I'll start with the easy run to begin with", he thought.
He was on holiday for two weeks giving him a much earned break from his high pressure job in Munich in an international bank. He loved the mountains and the snow and the freedom it gave him from the daily pressures of his work.
He slowly moved forward checking the markers for the start of his route down the mountain. It would only take him five minutes to get to the bottom of the slope, but he would relish every moment.
Then he pushed forward with his skis and started to glide on the fresh snow. Immediately he flet exhilarated as he started to ski down the slope, moving gently to the left and then slightly harder to the right. He passed hundreds of pine trees lining his route on either side. It was the perfect start for the perfect holiday. In no time at all he reached the end of his run and made his way over to the ski lift to come back up the slope.

In some places on Earth the water gets so cold that it freezes over and becomes hard and turns into ice as you have seen earlier in my report. Or the land becomes covered with the white stuff called "snow". In this type of environment, the humans travel over these surfaces in a different way. They put on special footwear called "ice skates" for moving on the frozen water and "skis" for moving over the frozen land. Again, they use their legs primarily to move, but this is a different type of movement as the land or ice is very slippery, and humans can easily slip over and fall down onto the snow and ice if they move on these surfaces too quickly. Thus, the humans need to have a lot of practice at this skill if they are to move over these surfaces safely. They even have sports events where humans compete against each other to see who can go the fastest over this terrain.

So, you can now see just how humans move about over the surface of the Earth in a basic way. This means that they can move anywhere they want to across the land. They can even walk through a stream or a river if it is shallow enough. When it is too deep to walk through, or they need to move through a lake or ocean, the humans have developed another form of movement which I will now tell you about.

Swimming

Location - Quebec, Canada - two boys are swimming in a lake

"Hey Carl!" shouted a boy of about twelve to his friend watching him on the bank. It was the middle of the summer holidays and the two friends had ridden out to the lake on their bikes from their homes in Quebe , five miles away.
"I bet you can't do this?!!" the first boy shouted as he bobbed up and down in the cool water. Carl looked out towards his friend called Joe, who jumped upwards out of the water and then dived down again going into the clear blue waters of the lake. He pushed forwards through the water with his arms, kicking with his feet and legs at the same time. Carl watched for a few seconds more and then dived into the lake and swam out to where Joe had made his duck-dive. He trod water, whilst his arms spread out over the surface of the water and

*looked all around him, but he couldn't see any sign of Joe.
Then all of a sudden Joe surfaced right behind him, laughing
and gasping for air at the same time. Joe pushed Carl in his
back, which forced him to swim as he lost his balance. The
boys then played a sort of water-based version of tag as they
swam happily in the lake.*

As the energy form of water is much different to the air energy
that is on the land, the humans have learnt to move differently
in the water. Instead of moving upright as they do on land,
they move mainly in a horizontal way just like the fish, as this
is the best way to cut through the water. They can move lying
on their backs, or on their fronts. To move they must make
their arms, hands, legs and feet move together in unison. This
is called "swimming" and is only done by a small amount of
humans as a whole, though potentially all humans could do
this if they wanted to.

The humans are unable to swim under the surface of the water
for long periods, unlike the fish, as they need oxygen from the
surface to help them breathe. The human body can only carry
a limited amount of oxygen when it is under water and so
humans can only stay there for a short period of human time.
In fact, they seem to swim further when they stay on the
surface of the water, as they are able to breathe in oxygen as
and when they need it.

Some humans have overcome the problem of swimming
underwater by creating a container that contains oxygen,
which will go underwater attached to their backs and help
them to stay there for much longer periods of time. In this way
they are able to be quite similar to the fish and explore the
unusual world that is below the surface.

So, humans can move about the planet on both the land and in
water using their bodies. What about humans moving above
the ground in the air, just like the birds and insects? Well, this
is not possible for humans to do, as their body design is not
suited to flying. They would need wings like the birds to do
this and the force of gravity is too great for humans to stay in
the air for any length of human time. Many humans have tried
during their time on Planet Earth to do just this, but each time

they have failed as they are not built in the same way as birds and some of the insects. Instead, they have created a vessel which can transport them through the air, which I will tell you about below.

Before I move onto humans moving around the Earth in different types of vessels, there is one more type of movement that the humans do using their bodies. It is a strange and unusual thing to observe as the humans do not move anywhere. They just stay in the same place most of the time and can only perform this type of movement when they are listening to another human creation called "music". I will go into more detail about this human creation later on in my report, but for now you will observe how this music involves different beats and rhythms having the effect of making the humans move in strange ways.

Dancing

Location - Croatia: a rave taking place in a warehouse

The heavy bass beat boomed out throughout the nightclub. It was so loud, so deep that the walls shook. The place was packed with young people all moving to the music in various ways. Some moved their arms as though they were swimming upwards from the deep sea, whilst others twisted and gyrated. Some held cans of coke and other stimulating drinks in one hand whilst the other hand was held high as if reaching up for air. Then everyone began jumping up and down in unison as the tempo of the music changed and the beat became quicker. Some of the revellers had been on the dance floor for hours and were starting to get exhausted. A few moved away from the middle of the throng and collapsed on the edge of the room, needing a necessary break from all the movement, their bodies drained of energy. But still the never ending beat went on and most of the dancers continued doing what they enjoyed, no matter what their bodies were telling them.

There is one form of movement that human beings practise as a leisure activity that you will find quite strange to observe. It is a movement which both male and female human beings make, as well as the young and the not so young. It is always done when the sound of music is happening, which influences the way that the humans move. There are even special buildings that the human beings have constructed for this practise that go by the name of clubs, ballrooms, and dance halls. The human beings call it "dancing" and when different types of music are heard they suddenly get up off their seats and start moving in the most unusual ways. They might move their arms in different ways or move their legs and feet in other ways. All the time their moving is being influenced by the different sounds of the music that they are hearing.

Some human beings appreciate the movements of other human beings so much, that they even have "competitions" where prizes are awarded for the ones who move better than the others as they practise this from of dance. The humans may dress themselves in all sorts of colourful and exotic clothes or costumes which are designed to show off their movements better.

Dancing is mainly done just for fun though, as the humans find that it helps them to relax and forget about the activity of work. This can be seen in the event-capture above where many humans gather together to practise this leisure pursuit. It is also associated with human celebrations like weddings or human rituals whereby all the human beings in a particular group partake of this activity.

Some humans say that it also helps to keep them well and healthy as they are constantly moving about and so making all their body parts work.

Now, it is time to tell you about the human concepts called "travel" and "transport" which involves the humans moving over the surface of the planet, either by themselves or in machines and vehicles that they have created.

Travel and Transport

"Travel" is basically the humans moving from one place to another, using energy to make this happen. Of course, we "travel" from one place to another without any effort, but the humans have developed different ways and means to do this. These are often quite primitive by our standards. From the beginning of human life on Earth, the humans have always moved around. They were a nomadic species from their earliest days, moving round from one place to another, using just their feet and legs.

Eventually they managed to get some of the animals like horses and donkeys to carry them in a process called "riding", where the human would sit on the back of the animal, which then walked or even ran to transport the humans from one location to another. These animals were also used to carry and move the objects and goods of the humans themselves. But gradually over the years the humans have created different vehicles that they use to carry or "transport" their bodies in. These can be utilised for travel on land, on sea, or in the air. Let me now tell you how these transport forms developed and how they work.

The Wheel

In more recent human times, human beings have gradually started to move faster and faster around the planet - by their standards. As I have just said they first of all moved with their bodies – either walking or running. But they still had the problem of how they could transport the objects which they needed to help them survive and develop. They began by putting these objects on wooden platforms, which they got their horses or donkeys to drag along the ground. This was slow and hard to do. Then they learnt that you could move the goods on a vehicle which had circular constructs called "wheels". This gave them the power to move themselves and objects across the surface of the Earth much quicker than before. In most cases they didn't have to use their legs and feet, as these vehicles were big enough to carry both humans and goods.

As they were able to move at greater speed than before, the use of the wheel developed into more advanced vehicles being created by the humans. These vehicles needed special energy to make them move, as well as a special surface on which to travel along the earth's surface. So, in the present human period you will see three main types of wheeled transport – the bicycle, the car and the train. I will now tell you more about them, as you will find these types of vessels all over the Earth, especially a vehicle called "the car", which has come to dominate the lives of many humans the world over.

Let us go into more detail here about these vehicles.

Road transport

Location: Surrey, England: the clockwise carriageway of the M25 Motorway

It was just after half past four in the afternoon. The traffic was heavy and ahead the speed limit signs were showing '60' for all four lanes of the M25 clockwise. Stephen Knowles was on his way to Heathrow Airport. He had a seven o'clock flight to Nairobi to catch. But would he make it? He knew he should have left earlier as this stretch of the M25 was notorious for hold ups. Yet he had been delayed by a phone call from the office on some minor, irrelevant matter.

He wished he could put his foot down as he passed the Chertsey exit, but the amount of traffic wouldn't let him. The next gantry had 50 mph signs, yet the traffic was going much slower than this. All around him were hundreds of frustrated motorists in their 4 x4's and their pickup trucks and their lorries, all slowing down.

The wall of red tail lights ahead was the final straw. He pressed the car's brake pedal and came to a stop. He decided to put the radio on in case there was some bulletin about what was happening. He heard the song, "The Road to Hell" playing. "How appropriate!" he thought. That was it. "By the

*time I get to Heathrow and park my car. I'm bound to miss my
check-in window. I thought these motorways were meant to
speed traffic up, not slow them down!"*

When the humans first discovered the use of the wheel they
could only make it move by forcing other animals like horses
or donkeys to pull the wheeled vehicles they had constructed.
They gave the names of "carts", or "chariots" or "coaches" to
different versions of the same fundamental design. These
vehicles needed two, three or usually four wheels to move
along the ground. Then humans learnt that you could use a
vehicle with two wheels to carry a human on, which the
human themselves would power. This object was called a
"bicycle" and was in many ways a better substitute than a
horse. But as it had just two wheels, it needed a new human
skill called "balancing" to work. As humans became more
confident and skilled at riding this two wheeled bicycle some
humans added a motor to it which meant you didn't have to
push the pedals with your feet. Instead, the motor made the
wheels move and this became the "motorbike" which could
travel very fast. The main problem with was that it didn't have
a cover over it to protect the driver from the wind and rain.

The next type of vehicle to evolve was one with four weeks
which could carry two or more humans in it. It was called a
"car" and had an engine powered by petroleum, which
powered it so it could move along the Earth without the driver
having to use his own energy. At first it was open to the sky,
but soon a roof covering was added which gave the driver and
passengers cover from the wind and rain and sun and other
types of weather. Cars could go quite fast, provided they had a
hard surface called a "road" to travel on. As more and more of
the cars were made, so more and more of the land was covered
by roads, so much so that in many places there are now miles
and miles of roads which have covered the natural land and
killed many of the animals that once lived there.
Humans have become obsessed with this vehicle, the car.
They spend hours cleaning them so that they shine in the sun.
They love to drive them at very fast speeds, sometimes
scaring and hurting other human beings and animals in the

process. They race their cars against each other. They crash them and then they get other cars to take their place. All the time their cars are sending out lots of pollution into the Earth's atmosphere and making the planet dirty. Then they all seem to go out in their cars together and end up being stuck in the same place in what the humans call a "traffic jam" as in the event-capture. Other humans choose not to use a car, or they simply cannot afford to buy a car, so they use other forms of transport, or even just use their own bodies to get about in the form of movement known as walking.

Apart from cars there are other road vehicles including "coaches", "buses", "lorries" and "vans", which are all bigger vehicles than a car. As more and more of these vehicles were built, they made them so that they could go at faster speeds and the humans thought that they had created a fine way of moving about. What they didn't realise was that these vehicles could be dangerous if they weren't used properly and soon many negative things happened. Some vehicles were driven into other vehicles when the driver wasn't looking where he was going, and the humans got injured or in some cases ended their earthly life. Or sometimes a human walking along got in the way of a vehicle and was injured or killed. This happened to humans of all ages, but it was especially tragic when a child's earthly life was ended.

This caused the humans to think why did we make such vehicles if this happens? But still the people who had the power to make these vehicles continued to make more and more of these vehicles and those who governed the people allowed this to happen. What happened next was that there became so many of these cars and lorries on the roads that they became still on the roads, usually after an accident, or just because so many people wanted to go along the same road at the same time.

Also, the petroleum that was burning in these vehicles' engines gave off a chemical gas called carbon monoxide, which made the air dirty and polluted the skies and gave some humans illnesses of the lungs like asthma and bronchitis. Still the humans with the power didn't stop these vehicles from being built. Then one day a human said we should stop making these vehicles and think of other ways to move about, but many of the humans who possessed these vehicles just laughed at him and continued to use their vehicles to travel even more slowly than they had before. As you know you can't just keep doing something more and more because eventually that thing will lose its energy and power.

But motor vehicles are not the only form of transport there is on Planet Earth. The other main one is called a "train". Let me tell you about this.

Trains

Location – North Yorkshire, England: a train on the Settle and Carlisle Line

The steam train gave a shrill whistle and pulled slowly out of Settle station, moving north. It was going to be a hard slog up the steep gradients of this railway line all the way to Carlisle. This stetch was known as "The Long Drag". It stretched for over fifty miles over the Yorkshire Dales, all the time going upwards on a gradient of 1 in 100. After twenty minutes the train had passed through Ribblehead station and the scenery was now wild and bleak. In the distance Pen-y- Ghent could be seen, black and silent against the dark grey sky. White steam left a trail in the sky, perfect for all those photographers dotted here and there along the line side, hoping for that special photograph. The passengers, enjoying the breathtaking scenery, were tucking into a four course meal, prepared on board by the expert catering team, Soon the train slowed as the track went from double to single as it entered the section of line which went over the Ribblehead Viaduct, constructed all those years ago by hundreds of navvies in dire conditions of cold, damp and hardship.
Once it was over the viaduct the train continued to climb upwards, passing through the remote Dent and Garsdale stations, as well as going through various tunnels until it finally reached the highest point of the line. This was Ais Gill Summit at 1169 feet above sea level. The fireman could now relax after putting loads of coal into the firebox. From now on

it would be plain sailing as the train descended in its route through Kirby Stephen and Appelby on its way to its destination at Carlisle.

Before the car took over as the most popular form of transport on the planet there was the "train". Although a human had discovered the circular object called the wheel, many years before this, it still took many human years for the transport form of the train to be discovered. Whilst humans had constructed vehicles which used the wheel these vehicles were very slow, but the burden they carried meant that humans could move their possessions much quicker and easier than before. The main difficulty they faced was that the track they moved these wheeled vehicles on was primitive and at times muddy. Eventually someone came upon with the idea of putting the wheeled vehicles on long strips of wood or iron called "rails" and a new form of transport was born.

To make the rail vehicles move faster the humans discovered the power of heating water to create "steam", which was very primitive as you had to burn lots of coal dug from deep under the ground to do this. Yet this primitive form of transport worked, as very soon "railways" as they became known, were built all over the land in many parts of the world. To achieve this a lot of land was dug out or destroyed to put the rails on, but the humans were happier as they could get to another place much quicker and could transport large amounts of possessions to other places sooner than before.

The other main way that humans move about is in a vessel that moves or "floats" on water called a "boat". There are millions of these boats found all over the planet and they come in all shapes and sizes. Here is one in action.

Water Transport

Location - The North Pacific Ocean: the bridge of an oil tanker ship

The large oil tanker, with a cargo of over five thousand tonnes of oil was now well on its way from Los Angeles to Tokyo. It was just over twenty four hours since the ship had left the USA bound for Japan on a North Westerly course. For the first time on the journey the ship's pilot could relax as the ship was now far away from land and clear of the busy coastal waters around the United States.

"Anything to report?" asked the captain, who had silently appeared behind the pilot who was standing at the bridge looking forwards.

"All clear ahead, Captain," he replied. "We've overtaken two slower vessels in the last hour and the way ahead is clear for the next hundred miles according to the radar."

"Anything to report on the weather?"

"No sir. It's a still, clear night with a wind speed of just two knots from the south east. The sea is the calmest I've known it for a good few years."

"Good. I think you can turn in for the night then," said the Captain, who was about to take over the night watch shift.

"Good night, Captain".

"Good night, Murray ".

With that the pilot left the bridge and walked along the deck towards his quarters. It was a warm, clear night and he paused for a few moments to look up at the night sky. There was just a slither of the new moon to be seen, but all over the sky, thousands of stars lit up the night, sending their light to the sea causing it to glisten as the swell of the waves moved up and down. The ship was making good progress.

As Planet Earth is covered mostly with water, the human beings soon learned that you can move over water if you build a vessel that floats on the surface of water. The speed at first was quite slow and depended on the humans using their own arms and hands to move the vessels or boats. Then they learned that they could harness the power of the wind to make their boats move and soon human beings were travelling great distances across the Earth's oceans.

From this event-capture you can see that humans are travelling over the surface of the oceans that cover the Earth. They have managed to build large vessels known as "ships" in which they transport all sorts of human made goods, as well as oil, gas, and coal in large quantities. This is on a large scale, but there are smaller boats that carry people - sometimes across seas and sometimes across rivers. The humans have even built artificial inland waterways called "canals" for their boats to sail along. These were built overland simply by many humans digging the soil out of the ground and depositing it elsewhere. In the gaps which were left they filled them with water so the boats could travel between towns and cities which were not previously connected to other rivers and seas.

Finally, there are even vessels that are able to travel great distances underwater called "submarines". They are like a giant human-made fish and can stay under the water for a long period of Earth time before they need to come back to the surface for air.

Now it is time to look upwards and see how humans move about in the air above the land surface.

Air Transport

Location - Alicante, Spain: passengers waiting to board their flight at an airport

The weary holiday makers were sitting patiently in the departure lounge at Alicante Airport, tired and in one or two cases still drunk from the night before. They had just spent the last two weeks on a cheap package holiday in the Spanish resort of Benidorm. Now it was time to head back home to Britain and reality. The sun shone dazzlingly bright through the large windows that gave a wide view of the runway. A passenger jet was waiting on the tarmac after being refuelled and "serviced" by the ground staff.
"Flight B356 is now ready for take-off. Will passengers kindly make their way to gate 14. Please have your passports and tickets ready for inspection", came the announcement in both English and Spanish. Immediately the weary travellers sprang into action. They were a mixture of young families, grandparents and twenty somethings. One by one they were

checked through the departure gate and then they trooped down the stairs, through a gate and onto the tarmac. They all had to wait as a lady in a wheelchair was carried up the steps and onto the plane first. Gradually they all filed up the steps and into their seats. Soon everyone was sitting down and waiting for take-off. The plane's engines roared into life and the captain spoke, "Good morning everyone. this is Captain Edwards speaking. You are on Flight B356 to Glasgow. We will shortly be taking off and expect to arrive in Glasgow around 15.45. And now the stewards will go through the safety procedure".

"Please make sure your safety belts are fastened and all hand luggage is stored in the baggage racks above your heads or in the space under your seats. In the event of a loss of cabin pressure, please release the oxygen masks from the seat in front of you, cover your mouth and breathe normally. There is a life jacket situated under the seat in front of you. Please inflate once you are in the water and use the whistle to blow for help if needed".

By now the plane was taxiing down the runway. A boy of about three was crying as he tried to get out of his safety belt as the plane suddenly lurched forward and gathered speed as it gently took off. In no time at all the plane was high above the Spanish coastline and cruising at 30,000 feet.

One of the activities that human beings had longed for ever since they had lived upon Planet Earth was to be able to escape the gravity of the planet and fly up above the land just as the birds do. At first they tried to emulate the birds by adding wings to their bodies, but of course as they were a completely different species, there was no way that the man made wings would work, as they weren't able to control the feathers in the same way that the birds could do. Inevitably the humans who tried this fell straight back down to earth and left their bodies.

Eventually another human being found out that if you could control certain gases that were lighter than the air that they breathed, they could go up into the air. So "balloons" were built which could easily lift a human up off the ground. The problem with this method at first was that you weren't able to control the movement of the balloon as the Earth winds would blow the balloon in different directions. Gradually this problem was overcome and larger balloons were built which could travel further and higher, but they were still limited in how far they could travel.

Then eventually humans learnt how to get specially built vehicles off the ground and up into the air. Unlike balloons the humans were able to control them much easier and could go up and down or to the left and right. Again, they couldn't go very far distance wise, but gradually more progress was made and soon these "aeroplanes" as they became known could fly further and faster. They eventually were able to fly higher than the birds themselves! Plus, they were able to fly not just over land, but over the sea as well. Suddenly the humans could reach other countries in a much shorter time than if they travelled over land.

The main problem was that they needed special fuel which came out of the ground, to fly. This, when burnt, gave these aeroplanes, or "planes" for short the power to travel at great speeds, which humans had never travelled at before and they could go further than other earlier flying machines. The other problem with burning their fuel was that it gave off a thing called "pollution" and it caused the air to become poisoned. I will explain more about this later on in my report.

Space Travel

For the penultimate part of my report on Human Movement I would like to show you the efforts of the humans to actually move themselves off the planet. Let me show you how they do it.

Location – Kazakhstan: a space rocket waiting to take off at a launch pad.

The team leader looked out from the control room towards the rocket on the launch pad. It was very nearly time for the rocket to leave the Earth and go into space with its payload of three different satellites belonging to various telecommunications firms. Well away from the launch pad a crowd of several thousand was eagerly waiting for the spectacle to begin. The launch had been postponed twice now due to problems with the weather, including high winds and storms. Today, the weather was perfect with a clear blue sky, illuminated by the bright sun shining over the barren wasteland.

The countdown clock showed two minutes to go and the various technicians and computer programmers started giving out different instructions and typing furiously into their computers. The noise from the crowd started to subside as they watched a close up of the clock on a giant screen. A flock of geese flew precariously close to the rocket, but at the last minute changed direction as they felt the heat emitted from the rocket's engines which had now been fired up. The team leader took out a handkerchief and wiped the sweat from his forehead and looked at the clock once more. Thirty seconds to go. The whole room went silent and still as the announcer started saying the magic words, "ten, nine, eight, seven, six". Large flames appeared from below the rocket and everyone held their breath.

"Five, four, three, two, one. Blast off!" The jaws holding the rocket in place had been released and the rocket slowly started moving upwards away from Earth climbing higher and higher, gradually getting smaller as it went. The crowd all cheered, as did all the ground crew in the control room. It had been a successful take off.

From this event-capture you can see that the humans use a mode of transport called a "rocket". This primitive contraption manages to escape the inner atmosphere of the planet but isn't capable of going much further. The humans have been constantly trying for many Earth years to travel throughout space, but they haven't so far exceeded, apart from very short distances away from their planet, including to their satellite, known as the "Moon". They have been hampered by the force called gravity which I have told you about earlier. They have not yet been able to develop anti-gravity vehicles which would allow them to travel further out into space. We, of course can travel throughout the universe with ease and have mastered these hinderances.

Some humans have become so desperate to travel through space that they have spent large amounts of human "money" to pay for the development of their space travel programmes. But the progress is very slow and they are a long way behind other races in the universe in learning to do this.

Disabled Humans

Before I finish this section of my report I must mention to you that there are some humans who aren't able to use their limbs and walk, or run, or swim, or do any of the other movements with their bodies that most humans can. These are often called "disabled" people. Let me show you an event-capture to help you understand.

Location - Lancashire: a disabled person travelling into Manchester by train

Matilda lifted herself into her wheelchair and said goodbye to her mother as she was placed on the lift by the taxi driver. After he had strapped her safely into place he drove her to her local railway station where she would catch a train into Manchester. At the station she bought her ticket and went through the gate which was held open for her by a thoughtful fellow traveller. Then she moved to the lift and descend down to the platform. She wheeled herself along the platform to where the yellow markings indicated where she would be able to access the train. Several people stared at her as if she were strange.

Within five minutes the eight-car train thundered into the station. She had pre-arranged for someone from the station to help her onto the train and immediately a man appeared with the metal slope which would connect the platform with the train entrance. Matilda thanked him as she accessed the train and then rolled the wheelchair into place by a bike rack. Then an alarm beeped to warn everybody that the train doors would be shutting.

The train moved off and everything went smoothly until she arrived at her destination station. When the train stopped no one was waiting to help her off the train. What should she do? Luckily two young males came to her rescue and asked her if she would like them to lift her off the train. As she had no other option, she said, "Yes". They did this, but Matilda was left fuming and frustrated. Yet again she had suffered because she was disabled and had been let down by the train company.

From the above event capture you can see how some humans find it difficult to move around the planet. They are not able to move in the same way as most of the other humans. They might be able to move part of their body in some way, but not as quickly or as efficiently as other humans. Or they might not be able to move at all because they are so ill that they have to stay in their homes all the time. There are many humans who are not able to walk at all and so they need a vehicle called a "wheel chair" to help them move about. This is like a seat for the human with two large wheels which transports the human around. Others have part of a limb like an arm or a leg missing, perhaps due to an accident, or because they were born in that form. Some of these humans may need a wheel chair or a walking stick to help them move, or in some cases they may be given a replacement limb part which helps them to move once more almost the same as the majority of the humans.

Sometimes humans might have the term "disabled" attached to them because of this lack of movement, but also it can be due to other things like not being able to hear or to see things as other humans can. Or it can be because of pain stopping them from moving or fear of falling over and injuring themselves. Most humans are sympathetic to them and try to help them if they need help, but other humans do not help them and even laugh at them because they don't understand them and their needs. This can be hurtful to these disabled humans and put them off from moving around the Earth.

Next I will tell you about how humans communicate with each other in various ways.

Part 4

Human Communications

E-mails and faxes straight from the heart.
News every hour - we've got the power.
We're living together, but worlds apart.
Why don't you talk to me?

Speech

The next aspect of being a human being on Planet Earth is the concept of communication. We ourselves have no need of this concept, as whatever we think, all of us think the same thing together. Yet, as human beings are separate from each other, they have all sorts of ways and means whereby they communicate their thoughts and information to other humans. Let me begin by showing you an example of the most basic form of human communication.

Location – Armagh, Northern Ireland: a mother teaching her child to speak

The young mother was holding her two year old son on her lap, looking at a colourful book of nursery rhymes. She started to sing out loud one of the nursery rhymes.
"One, two, three, four, five – once I caught a fish alive. Six, seven, eight, nine ten – then I let it go again!" Her son began to giggle loudly as he took in all the words his mother was singing. He tried to copy her. "On, too, fee, for, five", he repeated as best he could in toddler speak.
"Well done Leo!" his mother said, making sure that she praised him for his effort. "It's w-o-n Leo. Can you say that?" Immediately Leo tried saying "one" out loud but he could only say "on" once more.

"OK. Let's look at some of the pictures", replied the mother.
She pointed to a picture of a fish and said, "What's this Leo?"
Leo replied straight away. "Fis", he said, laughing as he said
it.
"Nearly Leo". It's fishhhh. Can you say that?
"Fishhh", copied Leo, clapping himself as he realised that he
had learnt to say a new word.
"That's a good boy. I knew you could do it!"

Human communications can take many different forms, but the most common form of communication on Earth is that of "speech" which uses "words" that come out of the human mouth. Words are actually different vibrations that the human creates in the mouth area of the human body. These words, when put together in a string, form a "sentence" and these are the basis of human speech. When humans speak to each other in this form of communication, it is usually by two humans saying sentences one at a time to each other. Several sentences put together is known as a "conversation". Usually these are quite pleasant as the humans exchange different ideas, news and their inner thoughts. However, humans can sometimes disagree with what the other human is saying and can get angry with each other and this is known as an "argument".
Quite often in arguments humans raise their voices so that they are speaking louder than they normally would in a conversation, and this is known as "shouting". The opposite of this is called "whispering", which is where the humans speak so quietly that you can hardly hear them speaking.

The way that humans say the words can vary at different places on the planet.
So, although we are all the same in our way of communicating the humans have another word for this and this is called "language". There are many thousands of these on Planet Earth and not one universal language as you would expect. This makes it very difficult at times for humans to communicate with each other. Let us see how speech in different languages works on Earth.

Languages

As I have already mentioned one of the main forms of communication between the human beings is the use of words. These are energy sounds that come from the human being's mouths. There are hundreds of thousands of different sounds that come from this source and when put together in a line they make sense to the humans although we may find them gibberish. You will find that the different racial types of human being have different sounds which are peculiar to them. This is their language and unless you are born into that particular human grouping you will not be able to understand what they are saying.

However over human time, the various human beings learnt to understand or "translate" what they were saying into their own language and the language barriers were broken down. Even within the different languages you get slight variations in the way that the words are pronounced. These are called "accents" and some humans within a particular group find it hard to comprehend what their fellow human is saying. There are hundreds of different languages found throughout the Earth, though some are more widespread than others. These include the ones the humans call English, Spanish, French, German and Mandarin.

In the next event-capture I will show you the problems that the humans have when they try to communicate with each other when neither human speaks the same language as the other human.

Location – Marrakech, Morocco: a flea market

Scores of copper coloured smoking pipes and pewter trays could be seen from the ground to the ceiling, crushed into the small room within the flea market. It was busy with tourists who were looking to haggle for a bargain from the many traders who plied their wares in this vast market area of Marrakech. Across the alleyway was a stall brimmed full of shoes and slippers of all sizes and designs – some purple, some gold, some lime. Next to this was room full of golden metallic objects – jugs, goblets, boxes and cups. It was this shop which caught the Austrian tourist's eye. Here was a place where he was sure to find something to take back to his mother.

He walked across the threshold and looked up and down the various shelves.

"Would you like to buy a pipe perhaps sir?" said the stall holder in broken French, pointing to the vast array of pipes, but the tourist didn't understand, as he didn't speak French. He shook his head indicating that he wasn't understanding the man.

The stall holder tried saying the same thing in English, but again he didn't understand. Instead, he pointed to the bowls and the shop owner immediately picked one up and said, "50 francs". The tourist ignored him and began to look at the goblets. He picked one up and asked the shop keeper, "How much?'" In Austrian.

The shopkeeper guessed what he was asking and held up his two hands with fingers outstretched indicating that it was 10 francs.

The tourist had been advised that it was always best to haggle in places like this, but he was getting fed up of the language barrier.

He nodded his head and replied, "OK". That was one word that everyone knew he thought.

The shop keeper held out his hand to show that he was sealing the sale. The tourist was puzzled at first, then realised what was going on and immediately shook hands with the shopkeeper. The deal was completed in spite of the language barrier.

From my research it seems that all humans originally communicated telepathically just like you and I do. Nowadays this skill seems to be absent from most humans as they seem to communicate by using sound waves which are created in the mouth area of their heads. You see, gradually over human time, the humans began to realise that you could make noises from your mouth by using your tongue, your teeth, and your throat, just as the birds and animals were doing. In fact, many humans learned how to copy the sounds of the birds and the animals until eventually the sounds from the humans evolved into words. There were just a few words at first that indicated basic human needs, such as "food", "home" or "danger".

Then the humans began to give a different sound and name to everything they could see around them such as "tree" or "water" or "mountain". This became human language and it was same wherever you went on Earth. But after the Change occurred one of the results was different languages being used in different areas around the Earth.

The natural result of this was that humans began to think of themselves as separate and different from other humans in other parts of the Earth. Plus, they started to see themselves as separate and unconnected with The Source and this has had very negative effects on Human Beings. In each area of the Earth where there were humans living, different speech patterns developed and this eventually led to languages being developed. All of this has led to people feeling divided and apart from each other because they speak in different tongues.

Gradually things have begun to change on Planet Earth with many humans starting to communicate with each other in spite of their different languages. I will go into these changes later on in my report, but for now I will show you another type of communication between humans, which like speech, comes out of the human mouth.

Singing

Location – Hamburg, Germany: a rock music concert

The crowd of two thousand souls were eagerly awaiting the start of the gig. The group they had come to see, hadn't played live for three years and had just released a comeback album that both the fans and the critics alike loved. There were a few whistles and slow handclaps as the tension grew. Then suddenly the lights in the theatre dimmed and a huge cheer went up as the bass drum banged out a thudding beat. Everyone was on their feet in an instant. Next a faster snare

*drum upped the tempo and then the bass came in with a deep
regular pulse. It was joined by the lead guitar with a couple of
power chords. The crowd cheered even louder. Finally, the
vocalist started singing his opening lines and the four men in
the group were as one with the audience.*

*Whilst all this had been happening scores of fans had rushed
down to the stage so they could be nearer their heroes.
Flashes from cameras and mobile phones were going off and
the people at the front were lunging forward with their arms
outstretched. Many were rocking their heads in time to the
beat of the music and some were clapping with their arms
above their heads. Most of the audience were now singing
along to the lyrics of the song which they all knew by heart.
When it was the chorus they all sang, "La, la, la" as one. It
was business as usual for both group and audience. Everyone
was ecstatically happy.*

From the above event-capture you can see that humans have
another way of releasing words from their mouths. This is
completely different to speaking, as it involves changing the
sounds that come out of the mouth into a different pitch and
tone. This type of human activity is known as "singing" and
the words they use in this when put together are called
"songs".

With singing, the sounds that come out of the human throat
are different than the sounds of human speech. They form a
"musical" as opposed to a "spoken" sound. They both come
from different vibrations made in the throat, but with human
singing the different vibrations it causes the sounds to be of a
different form. One difference is that the range of sounds is
more wide ranging. This has the effect of creating a version of
the human creation called "music". I will tell you more about
this in another part of my report. For now, I will say that these
musical sounds have the effect of making the humans have the
emotion of "happiness". In fact, they will very often join in
with the singing that they hear by singing the same song that
they hear, as in this event-capture.

Humans love to sing. Sometimes they will sing along to a
piece of music or song that they are listening to. Sometimes
they will sing the words of a song without any music playing

because that sog has remained inside their head. Sometimes they will just sing some words because they are happy. When several humans get together to sing this is known as a "choir". Humans also love to hear other people sing as you have seen in this event-capture which is known as a "concert" or "gig". As you will see later on music is an important part of human life.

Now, let us look at another form of communicating that the humans do. This again with the use of words, but in a different way.

Writing

Many eons ago, humans put the spoken words into a human invention called "writing". This is where you get various scripts which are formed by a stroke of the pen or brush to make "letters" or words. These were originally written down on stone, but the humans have evolved from stone via papyrus and paper to electronic screen, though paper seems to still be the main tool where human words are written down. Sheets of paper put together to form human inventions called "newspapers", "magazines" and "books". These are then "read" by the humans who retrieve the information that is written down in them and ingest it into their brains where it is digested and processed. Here is an event-capture where you can see an example of books and humans reading them.

Location - Helsinki, Finland: a public library

The mother and her two children aged four and six entered the large library. It was full of all sorts of colourfully bound books as far as the eye could see. The eldest child, a boy, started running to where the children's section was. He had been here many times before and was excited at the thought of finding a large colourful book with a story that would catch his interest. His younger sister was more timid. She held tightly onto her mother's hand as they walked sedately over to where the boy was now sitting, holding a book in his hands. It was a big

colourful book, full of pictures of various trains all moving around on a railway in a faraway land. The locomotives all had large smiles on their faces which the boy loved to see. He eagerly read aloud the writing in the book. "Shhh!" whispered his mother as she held a finger to her mouth. "Don't forget this a library. You have to keep quiet!"
Meanwhile the little girl had chosen another colourful book. This one was full of pictures of horses and unicorns, all with golden hair. She sat down on a tiny seat and placed her book onto a small table next to where her brother was already sitting. Whilst the two children were engrossed in their books their mother quickly chose a historical novel from a shelf nearby. After about ten minutes she gathered up her two children and took the books to be scanned. Everyone was happy with their choice of book.

Here you can see a large gathering of books together in one place which is called a "library". Here humans can come and visit this building which is open to anyone who wants to come into it. Once inside they are able to choose from thousands of books on all different subjects so that they can learn more about something, find the answer to a question they may have, or simply read a book for their own entertainment and pleasure. They are able to stay in the library all day if they wish to, or they can take away a book or several books to read at their own house or whilst they are travelling somewhere such as on a train or an aeroplane.
The books inside the library are provided by the local council or the government and so the human reading the book can read it for free without having to pay any money for the privilege of doing so. The books are divided up into two main types – "fiction" and "non-fiction". Fiction books are stories that are made up by the person who has written them and tell stories of anything the humans might do in their lives. They can be about real events, or alternatively they can be made up, which is called "fantasy". Many humans like reading these sorts of books as they help them to forget the real world that they live in and so take them to another world that they wouldn't normally live in. With non-fiction books the information inside them is about real things and how they work, or about

certain humans and what they have achieved with their lives. These are not as popular as fiction books but serve a useful purpose for humans who want to find out more about a certain subject or human.

Books written by humans are not just found in libraries, but they can also be bought by humans in "bookshops" where there are also lots of books together in one place. Sometimes books can give humans ideas about changing something in the country they live in on Earth. In a way the words in books can change the way the humans think and behave and so various human groups have tried to stop other humans from reading the books and newspapers that they produce. This is called "censorship" or "banning" and this only makes the humans want to read these banned items even more! There are other human inventions which contain words like books but they are completely different to books. Let me show you these.

Newspapers and magazines

Location – Sydney, Australia: the office of a tabloid newspaper

How's it going?" asked the editor to the figure hunched in front of his computer screen.
"A bit slow, boss", replied the young male reporter. "I've tried ringing the guy's missus up, but she's not answering her phone".
"Well get your butt round to her house ASAP and see what the story is!", snapped his boss. "If you can't get anything out of her, just make something up!"
Over on another desk a young woman was typing frantically on her keyboard. She was writing up her report about a murder trial which had just finished. The defendant had been found guilty by the jury and had been sentenced to life imprisonment, with a minimum term of thirty years. She had managed to get quotes from the victim's family, but the murderer's family had been quite abusive to her when she had asked them a question and had not given anything away. She decided to put in a few words of her own to fill in that gap.

She needed a thousand words to put in her space in the newspaper.
In the editor's office, the editor was looking at the layout of the next day's edition and was getting worried. There was not enough copy to fill the thirty-two pages. Nor were the advertising department doing enough to get advertising space filled up.
"How on Earth was it all going to be sorted in time?", he thought. "Why do I bother?" He knew that above him was the newspaper proprietor waiting to give him the push should he not get results.
"Pressure. It's all pressure and I'm getting sick of this", he thought.

The event-capture you have just seen shows a human place where a thing called a "newspaper" is created. This is like a book in that it is filled with many words, but it is not a long as a book in the majority of cases. Instead, it is much flatter and is made up solely of paper pages as opposed to having a cover. It also has several photographs inside it, which are used to help the person reading it understand it more. As the name suggests it contains news and events that that are happening to different humans in different parts of the planet.

Once the newspaper is put together with all its stories, photographs and adverts, it will be checked for mistakes and then sent off to be printed. Tens of thousands of copies of the newspaper will be printed and then distributed to many shops all over that region, or country. Then individual humans will come into the shop and buy the newspaper, or in some cases will have it delivered to their home address by a "newspaper boy or girl". The humans will then read the newspaper and ingest all the information contained inside it into their brains.

There is another piece of communication-information that humans read which is like a newspaper, but which has a lot more photographs inside it and which tends to concentrate on a particular subject. This is called a "magazine" and is smaller in size to a newspaper, though it may have more pages inside it. Also, it is a lot more colourful with many colour photographs inside it and on its cover.

Both newspapers and magazines are meant to publish the latest news and trends about what is happening in the world, but sometimes they are not completely truthful and can print made-up stories as in the event-capture above.

Sometimes the newspaper will be found out by someone reading it that it isn't the truth they are reading and sometimes they might not get caught. But most humans reading these publications can guess which is the truth and which isn't.

The main problem with newspapers is that they usually publish the news the day after it has happened. But many people now read the news on their computers and on the internet almost as soon as the news happens. So less and less people are buying these newspapers and one day in the human's future these newspapers will cease to exist in this form. I will tell you more about the internet and computers in my report below.

Telecommunications

In this next section of my report, I want to explain how humans use other forms of communication which have been created by the humans. These use various signals which are transmitted by wires and through the airwaves. They are telephones, radios and televisions.

Telephones

The humans have communicated with telephones for many years now and gradually over time they have become more sophisticated. Originally one human spoke words into a basic contraption which was connected to another contraption by wires where the other human could listen to what he was saying.

Gradually the distance between the two contraptions which came to be called "telephones" grew and grew by means of more longer wires. Eventually most adult human beings had a telephone in their homes and they could speak to other humans in other places thanks to the wires that connected them together. Then a human developed this system so that the sound waves between the two telephones didn't need wires anymore. Instead, they used satellites up in space orbiting the Earth to catch the sound waves from the telephone call and send them back down to Earth to another telephone in a different place. This meant that the telephone didn't have to be attached to a house or other building but could be moved about or become "mobile". In fact, it came to be called a "mobile phone" or "cell phone" by the humans as it could be carried around and used anywhere on the planet where it could pick up a signal to send it to a satellite. Let me show you this in action.

Location – Birmingham, England: the 'quiet carriage' of a train on its way into the city

The railway carriage was half full as it sped north through the outer suburbs of Birmingham, on its way to the main station. Most of the passengers were not looking out of the window, but down at their mobile phones, playing games, sending texts or looking at social media. A mobile phone started to ring and a teenager called Sophie swiftly lifted it from her handbag and pulled the earphones away from her ears. She looked at the screen in front of her. It said "Mum", indicating who was calling. She pressed the green button and said, "Hello Mum. What's up?"
"I just wondered what time train you'll be catching back tonight?" asked her mother, "And do you want me to pick you up at the station?"
Sophie replied, "I don't know yet. It all depends on what time the movie finishes. I'll text you when the train starts leaving".
"Do you want a lift, though?" persisted her mother.
"No. I'll catch a taxi, so you can go to bed. Don't wait up for me! Bye"
Just then a middle aged man in a dark suit came over to Sophie and said sternly, "You do realize that this is a quiet carriage and you shouldn't be using your phone?"
Sophie looked blankly at the man and then ignored him, putting her earphones back where they had been. She then went back to her mobile phone. She quickly tapped in a

message to her best friend, Freya. "C u in 10 mins." A couple of bleeps later the message had been sent and she waited for the reply. Precisely twenty seconds later Sophie's phone bleeped twice and her friend's message appeared, "Wl b l8. prb bt 20 mins". "Ok" was the reply that Sophie tapped in, before going back to the music that was playing through her headphones.

From the event-capture here you can see that the human is using a mobile phone, both to speak to her mother and to send a message to her friend which is called a "text". In fact, in more recent years humans tend to use their mobile phones to send texts, rather than to actually speak with another human being. You will also notice that on the train lots of people were using their mobile phones, not just to send texts, but also to look at the screen and observe various things like movies, puzzles, and information. This is because the mobile phones that humans are using nowadays contain not just the software to send messages and to speak to another human being, but they also contain a small computer which I will tell you about below.

There are now billions of these mobile or cell phones on the planet which has had the effect of making the humans come closer together, and not be apart as they used to be in the past. Many human beings have one of these phones and wherever you go on Planet Earth you can see the humans using them - sometimes as they walk along the road, sometimes as they drive cars, or just sitting down on a seat and using them. Not only do they use them to make telephone calls and to access information but they also use them to take photographs or to make their own films or movies. In fact, in the early 21st century of the human era most humans use their mobile phones more than they use books or watch the television.

After the telephone was invented by the humans, the next telecommunications form was the radio, which I will tell you about now.

Radio

Location – Limerick, Ireland: a person listening to a radio

Laura poured the boiling water into a mug which was standing on her kitchen worktop. She added a tea bag and went over to the fridge whilst the tea was brewing. In the background her radio was tuned to a greatest hits show which was coming to an end. She hummed along to the music as she opened the fridge and got hold of a carton of milk. The song that was playing on the radio reminded her of her younger days and how she would often dance to this song.
"Well, that's me, Andy L, signing out until tomorrow", said the DJ. "I hope you've enjoyed today's selection and it his brought back some good memories for you. See you same time tomorrow".
With that, a jingle for the radio station filled the kitchen as Laura lifted the tea bag out of the mug and then poured some milk into the brown, boiling liquid. She needed to hurry if she was to catch the 12 o'clock news headlines.
A couple of adverts for the latest car and a supermarket were coming over the airwaves as she put the milk back into the fridge. She grabbed a couple of rich tea biscuits from the biscuit jar on the work top and then made her way into the lounge where the radio was situated.
She sat down in her favourite chair just as the midday beeps from the radio filled the room.
"I am Chris Osbourne", said the announcer. "Here is the midday news"………..

From the above event-capture you can see a human listening to a radio contraption. This is a type of receiver which receives the signals sent out by the radio station across the airwaves. The human calls this box receiver a "radio", but radio does not just refer to the box, but to the whole creation of radio waves which transmit across the planet in the sky above the Earth. The radio waves carry all sorts of information which the listener can hear and take in through their ears. Most of the time this may be music which I will tell you about in another part of my report. But it can also be information in the form of news bulletins or adverts telling the listener about a new product.

The humans don't just listen to a radio in their own homes though. They can also listen to the radio as they travel along roads in their vehicles, or on trains or ships or even aeroplanes in some cases. For many years listening to the radio was a popular human activity as it helped the humans to forget about their everyday lives or learn some new and useful information. But this invention which was just audible would eventually be superseded by another one which was both audible and visual. This is where the box like object known as a "television" came into its own, which I will now tell you about.

Television

Location – Prague, Czech Republic: a woman watching a television talk show

The woman sitting in the comfy chair of her living room was looking forward to the next programme on the TV tonight. It was one her favourites and was one where a person interviewed dysfunctional families about their unusual lifestyle choices. Although it had been filmed in the USA, it was beamed all over the world via satellite and was easily obtainable in her country.

The programme began and focussed on a thirty-something woman on the low stage in front of the studio audience. She nervously fiddled with the rings on her left finger. She looked up and down at the TV chat show host, who held a thin grey microphone in his right hand and a clip board with some notes on it with his left hand. To her left sat her estranged husband, who looked straight at the audience, angst on his face. Behind him were two burly security guards, ear pieces sticking out of their ears, their arms folded as though saying, "Don't mess with us" On the TV screens ten million viewers watching could see the words, "I'M PREGNANT BY MY HUSBAND'S FATHER"

The chat show host lifted his microphone to his lips and said, "Well I've heard enough from you, Caroline. I think it's about

time we brought in your father-in-law to give his side of the story..."

On the far end of the stage, Caroline's father-in-law started to walk towards her, as the audience booed and whistled in disgust. Immediately, Caroline's husband leapt from his seat and was attacking his father before the security guards could stop him.

"That's more like it!" said the woman watching as the action unfolded. "I like a good fight!". She tucked into a sandwich and rewound the programme with her remote control, so she could watch the violent altercation again. After about ten minutes she got bored with the programme and started flicking through all the various channels on offer. After about twenty flicks she stopped and started watching one of the those selling programmes. But that was boring, so less than five minutes later she began to flick through yet more programmes until she found something she liked.

Various humans took the idea of radio waves a step further with the invention of the television. Instead of hearing something come out of a box that they could listen to, they could now watch moving pictures with their eyes as well as hear what was being said. They could also watch this television set in the comfort of their own homes. Instead of having to go out to a cinema or movie theatre to watch moving pictures they could watch the moving pictures in their own homes. The television sets they looked at were on a much smaller scale than in a cinema. Yet they became so popular that gradually more people started watching the televisions in their own homes rather than going out to the cinemas to watch the moving pictures.

At first the television programmes just had black and white as the only colours to show the moving pictures, but eventually every colour available was used. Plus, at first there were just one and then two or three channels for the humans to watch, but nowadays there are hundreds of different channels available. The subjects were also quite limited to begin with – news and drama. But today there is every possible subject shown on the television including sports, travel and nature programmes. Also, some programmes are only suitable for the older humans to watch and so laws came in to make sure that certain programmes were only shown at times when younger humans would not be watching. Also, it became possible to watch programmes on a television throughout the whole day for twenty four hours. Also, most humans have access to a television set all over the world, even if they don't own one. The way that television has changed and developed has been mainly due to the invention of the "computer" which I will now tell you about.

Computers

Location – Bergen, Norway: the house of a professional couple

Lars and Brigitte were at home sitting on the sofa. They had just finished their evening meal. The television was showing a detective programme, but neither of them was watching it. Lars had his laptop on his knees and was typing a name into a search engine. He wanted to find out what had happened to one of the actors on the TV programme. The required information soon came up. Then he started looking up the biography of the actor's wife. Momentarily he looked back to the TV programme to catch up on the plot.
Meanwhile Brigitte had her tablet in her hand and was playing a video game where you had to grab different coloured flowers and put them into a vase. Once you had managed to get ten of the flowers into the vase you could then go onto the next level. After about ten minutes of this she got bored and began to look at her favourite social media website. She giggled as she read one of the posts from her two hundred plus friends. Someone had put the face of a well-known politician onto the body of a film celebrity. Then she started to make a comment on what she saw. Lars was back on his lap top now, looking for information on sailing boats, one of his favourite hobbies. Then he started playing a card game until he got bored with that. Neither of them spoke a word to each other.

Computers are really just like the human brain as they can store vast amounts of Information – in fact they store whatever information the humans choose to put into them. They have grown in use from very basic ones to the most intricate and complicated ones now in use on the planet. At first the computers were very large so they could take in the information that the humans programmed into them. But then gradually they shrank in size to the ones that humans use today with names like "lap top" and "tablet" as in the event-capture. They are able to have vast memories which are all contained in what the humans call a "microchip", a tiny piece of hardware with a massive memory.

So, the computers today on Planet Earth can have all sorts of uses for the humans such as being able to solve complicated mathematical problems, play a song or a movie on the screen, hold the details of your bank account, or store your collection of photographs or films. Basically, they can mimic everything that a human needs in their everyday life. I would add that all this has been made possible by a revolutionary communications system that came into being only quite recently in human history. This is a system called "the internet" and I will tell you all about it now.

The Internet

The Internet is the one thing that seems to be having the effect of uniting the human beings. Its main use seems to be that of communication and this means that anyone, wherever they are in the world can make a connection with another human being in a different part of the planet through their computer in conjunction with the internet.

It is only in very recent human existence on Earth that the humans have started to achieve the sense of oneness that they had when they first existed on Planet Earth. After this oneness of human spirit was lost and subsequently forgotten about after the event called the Change, human beings went through a long period of separateness which they are only just beginning to see and understand. As a result of being separated from each other the humans have come to see other humans as separate and apart from them. They no longer saw other humans as being the same as them, but rather as different and separate from them. This lead to lots and lots of separation on a grand scale with things called fighting and wars taking place, which I will explain about later on in my report.

For now, this feeling of separation from other humans has started to weaken as many human beings have started to wake up to the fact that they are not separate from each other as they have been led to believe. Instead, they are learning and experiencing the fact that all human beings are fundamentally the same. The one thing that has taught human beings this fact has been this invention called the Internet.

The Internet is like a giant brain for the whole Earth and is a way of instant mass communication that we have always had and known on our planet. Through the Internet the humans have been able to find out what is happening on another part of the Earth which is many miles away from them. In the past news of an event on the other part of the world would have taken many months or even years to reach other humans. Now through image-capture that happening is sent instantaneously to other humans all over the earth through the internet. Not only that, but humans using the internet are able to learn about anything that exists on Planet Earth that they care to know about.

However, there are still many humans who are separate from other humans who use the internet in a negative way as you will now see.

Location - Moscow, Russia: an office filled with computers and their programmers

Alexi was hard at work in a top secret room in a large office block in a suburb in Moscow beavering away on his lap top. He had managed to hack his way into a US government department and he was busy transferring the information in front of him into the catch-all net which would be stored in another top secret room in another building in another suburb of Moscow. As soon as he had copied all the information on the site he would type on his keyboard certain lines of script which would have the effect of sending a damaging virus into the US website. As he typed furiously away his screen suddenly went blank. "Damn!" he shouted. All around him his work colleagues started swearing, banging their fists on their desks and causing a great commotion. The Internet signal had cut out for the third time that day. Now everyone would have to start again and hope they could complete their work without any more disruptions.

The above event-capture shows you that many humans are still separated from each other. Here one set of humans are hard at work trying to stop what another set of human beings are doing. This is because they have a different belief system to the other human beings, mainly because they live on a different part of the planet from them. They are basically afraid of each other and because they are different in some way to them they want to try and stop them. They will use the internet to do this, If they have a different belief system they will do things differently and they may not like the way other humans behave and feel threatened by them. As this idea grows it can lead to physical fighting between two groups of people and on a grand scale between two different countries with different ideas about how they want to live on Planet Earth.

Other ways of communicating

Finally, as I finish off this part of my report, I must add that there have been lots of other ways that humans have communicated with each other without spoken words, long before all of the above methods were discovered. Some of these included the use of flags, smoke, the sun, birds and so on. Apart from the above methods that the humans communicate with each other, there are some other ways of communication that have been developed to help some less able humans. Here are some of them.

The first is called "sign language" and is a way of communicating for the humans who are not able to either hear the words spoken by other humans or are not able to speak words themselves. It works by a human using its hands and fingers moving in different ways to indicate different words. So, when these humans see these hand signals they understand what the other human is communicating. This use of sign can be in hundreds of different human languages.

Then there is another way of communicating used by the humans who are known as "blind", meaning that they are unable to use their eyes to see fully or not at all. Although they may be able to hear the words said by other humans they cannot see what is going on around them. So, they use the sense of touch to read information or instructions on raised letters and symbols known as "braille".

Now that I have given you an idea of the basic human notion of language and communication, in the next part of my report I will look at how the humans actually get on with each other and the relationships they have.

Part 5

Human Relationships

Through the eyes of a child, there's no wrong or right,
No reason to hate, no need for a fight,
No colour, no creed, no malice, no greed....
'Till the child becomes a man

Human Relationships

So far we have seen how the human body works, how the humans move about and how they communicate with each other. Now it is time to see how humans interact with each other and how they react to the natural world around them. In fact, humans can react to each other in all sorts of strange ways as you will see. But first I must tell you about how the humans change in both body and mind as they spend more time on the planet and how they react to the world and other humans around them at these different stages.

So far, you have seen the form that the human takes when they are first born into a body on Earth and in the following few years. Now it is time to look at the stage known as childhood.

Childhood

Location – Rhyl, North Wales: a children's playground

Alice and Emily rushed up to the gate that opened into the children's playground. They were very excited as it was their weekly visit to the playground where they could let off some steam. It was a bright sunny day, with a clear blue sky above them and luckily for them there were no other children playing there today. Their mother called out, "Be careful!", but the two girls didn't notice what she said as they made their way onto the slide. They were up the stairs in an instant and shouted, "Wheeeee!" as they slid down the slide. They did this three times and then moved onto the roundabout. Without waiting to be asked, their mother came over from her seat and began to move the roundabout in a clockwise direction. "Faster!" shouted Emily. "Faster!"

"No that's quite enough!" said mum firmly. The girls began to get dizzy and Alice said, "I don't like this!" Instantly mum grabbed one of the metal rails and tried to slow it down, but the momentum carried her along with it. She quickly let go of the rail, deciding that it was safer for her to leave it to slow down by itself.

Next they moved onto the swings. Mum knew what to do and took it in turns to push the girl's seats so that they could get as high as possible.

"This is great!" shouted Alice, whilst Emily was silent, trying to be like her older sister, but really liking the height the swing was reaching.

After about ten minutes, mum said, "I think we all need a break", so reluctantly the girls made their way over to the bench that mum was sitting on and sat down beside her. After about two minutes they'd had enough and rushed over to the slide to continue with the proceedings.

After the baby/toddler stage of development the next stage is when the humans become what are known as "children". In this stage the human will continue to grow in size, getting bigger as a child. Then it will move through childhood and adolescence, until it becomes a fully grown adult human being. These stages usually last around twenty years, though it varies with each human being.

The human child will look like a miniature version of the adult human being, quite often looking similar to either its mother or its father. Yet it will still think and act as a child. This is because it possesses a human quality called "innocence" which children lose when they develop into the next stage. Innocence means that a child sees the human world in a much simpler way that the adult humans.

For a human child, everything is new and wonderful, fascinating and interesting. They will not be aware of other humans and think that the world revolves around them. They may well be unaware of other children's feelings and may hit out at their parents if they don't get their own way. They will need to be educated about what are the best and the worst ways to behave. The child is really like a container ready to be filled with information about the planet.

It is at this stage that a child will be moulded with all that it experiences from its parents and its brothers and sisters, and other human beings that it comes into contact with. These experiences could be positive or negative and will stay with that child throughout its whole life. A child has a basic instinct called "trust" within it, when it will unquestionably believe all that it is told or accept all that happens to it. The child will also not have any sense of danger and will do things without thinking, unlike an adult human who knows more about life and its dangers. This is why it is important for other parents including its parents to educate and teach them about the dangers of doing certain things, such as crossing a road, or jumping down from a high wall.

A child will rely on its parents to protect them and educate them, to guide them and tell them the best way forward in life. Sometimes the parents will do this properly as they should, but in some cases the parent will neglect to educate and guide the child in how the life on Earth works.

Gradually the child will grow and develop into a larger human being that is no longer a child, nor not quite an adult. The humans call this type of human an "adolescent" or "teenager" and it is the most difficult part of human life for many human beings until they settle down with the body or "vessel" that they live in. Let me show you an example of an adolescent human.

Adolescence

Location - Chicago, USA: the bedroom of a suburban house

The fifteen year old girl put down the celebrity magazine and went and stood in front of the mirror in her bedroom. All the walls in her bedroom were covered in glossy posters of different celebrities – pop starts, film stars and fashion models - all smiling, all slim and all wearing a face perfectly contoured and tanned.
"Why can't I be like them?" she thought. "I bet they've got friends who care for them. I bet they've got a nice boyfriend who treats them special". The girl herself was just as thin as the models in her posters, if not more so. She then rushed to the toilet and began to make herself sick, but nothing would come. She went back to her bedroom and started to cry, thinking of the cruel comments some of her classmates had said to her about her looks and her size earlier that day, She hated being called "loser" and "freak" and "retard" by the bullies and didn't know what to say back to them when they called her these names. After a few minutes she wiped her tears away and went back to stand in front of the mirror once more. "Why does life have to be so hard? So cruel?" she thought. Then she went back to her bed, lay down and picked up a different magazine to look at.

Here we are looking at an example of the human stage called "adolescence". This is the most difficult stage of human life for many human beings because they are no longer a child and still not yet an adult. They are somewhat confused about who they are. It is also the stage when there are many physical and chemical changes taking place inside the human body, which if not supported by an adult human being, cause the young human being to become quite anxious and at times angry and afraid.

For instance, the adolescent human being will think nobody loves them or cares for them. They will feel quite alone on Planet Earth and in many cases will be "bullied" by other adolescent human beings. This is where they tease or even hit one particular human being because they think they are different to them or perhaps because they simply don't like them. This causes much mental pain for the human being who is being bullied and hinders their emotional growth as a human being. If the human who is being bullied is not helped by other more mature human beings they cannot develop fully as they should do.

It is also at this stage that the human aspects of feelings and emotions start to really surface in human beings. These include all sorts of emotions that the human being shows such as Happiness, Fear, Anger, Hatred, Lust, Greed and Envy. They are all about how one human being responds to another human being. I won't go into detail about these feelings just yet, as you will see all the way through my report that these various feelings come to the surface in the different activities that human beings do.

Adulthood

It seems strange that some human beings do not progress beyond the childhood stage in their minds due to various reasons, but those who progress through this stage continue to grow and mature, until they evolve into the next stage. This is called the "adult stage" and lasts for about forty to fifty human years. This is what human beings call "the prime of their life" and is when they achieve what they have come to Earth for – their "life's purpose" as some human beings choose to call it. There are all sorts of activities that the human beings do at this stage of their lives which you will read about in the rest of my report. Most of them are positive actions, but sometimes there are negative actions that the human beings go through too.

The older human beings then evolve into another stage known as "middle age" where the humans continue to live as adult humans, yet they start to "slow down" as they put it. This is because their human body is starting to wear out and parts of their bodies such as hips, knees, ears or eyes need replacing or improving in various ways. They are still living normal human lives in most cases, but just don't have as much energy as the younger human adults. Most of them stop the activity called "work" at this stage, but some humans still continue with this activity into the next stage which I will now tell you about.

I will now quickly mention the final stage for a human being and that is called "old age" by most humans and it refers to the humans who have lived much longer than the adult human beings.

Old Age

Location – Bilbao, Spain: a terminally ill old man in a hospital room

The old man was getting weaker by the minute as the life gradually ebbed from him. On either side of his bed were his two daughters and his son, all aware that death was imminent. The heart monitor to the right of his head was showing a steady beat of sixty beats per minute, but his lungs were struggling to breathe in the oxygen that came down a tube and into a mesh across his mouth. The years of smoking countless cigarettes had finally taken their toll on his body. Now the cancer cells in his lungs were about to win the final battle inside him.

Very slowly he lifted his right hand and his eldest daughter held onto the bony hand. He tried to speak but he found it so hard to open his mouth, let alone speak the final words that he wanted to say. Slowly the words, "I love you" were uttered for one last time. Then the heart monitor stopped its regular beat and the alarm started sounding. All three of his children knew that it was the end.

Eventually the human beings reach the final stage of their existence on Earth, which is the old age stage which lasts for about ten years or more. Here the human beings spend most of their days in reflection, thinking about what their human existence has meant for them. During this stage the human being's bodies start to weaken and decay rapidly, depending on how they have treated their body in earlier years. Then there comes the point when the human body stops working and the energy or life force inside the body leaves the Earth.

This is what the humans call "death" and I will explain about this is more detail at the end of my report. Sometimes there are some human beings who leave the Earth at the earlier stages, as this is what they decided before they came to Earth, but for most human beings they will go through all the various stages of life before they leave. This is so they can experience as much as the Earth as is 'humanly' possible if you know what I mean!

Now it is time to look in detail at how humans react to other humans in different ways. I will begin with the most important one of all.

Love

There is one aspect of being a human being on Planet Earth which makes the humans unique in the Universe and that is the emotion called "love". Let me show you an example of love in action.

Location - Rome, Italy: a teenage boy and girl walking through a park

The two teenagers walked hand in hand under a row of sycamore trees that lined the walkway. Antonio was nineteen and Flavia eighteen. They had known each other for the past five months and were rapidly falling in love. Birds were singing and flying about amongst the branches, which had the first blossoms of spring growing from their buds. In the distance you could hear the noise of the Rome traffic with horns beeping every few seconds. But Antonio and Flavia were oblivious to those sounds. They came to a bench and sat down. Antonio looked into Flavia's eyes and said, "You coming into my life has changed me for good!" Flavia looked back at him and kissed him gently on his lips. "I love you forever, Antonio!" A shudder went through his body on hearing those words. They kissed passionately and then stopped to look into each other's eyes again. Then they hugged each other tightly. Neither of them had ever experienced anything like this before, although they had both been out with members of the opposite sex before. This love that they were feeling was completely overwhelming. They both hoped that it would never end.

Love is the most powerful emotion that human beings have inside them which affects everything that they do. There are all sorts of love emotions that the humans have which show themselves in various ways, but the main emotion of love works like this. It is a connection of well-being and positive vibrations of emotional energy that is passed from one human being to another. This means that the human being has the utmost respect and admiration for the other human being and will do anything to please them and make them happy. This state of being is known to the humans as "being in love" which you have just seen in the event capture. When this occurs mutually between two humans, this is one of the best feelings or emotions that human beings can have. This human experience can last a human lifetime or it can be for just a short while. It all depends on how much each human being is committed to the other human being.

Sometimes the emotion of love can be shown in other ways, such as a human parent loving their child or their pet, or a human being loving an activity that it practises, or a place on Earth that it visits, or a food that it eats. In fact, loving something or someone can make the human being have a feeling called "happiness" which is the state that all human beings once were in, but at this time in their history, very few have that feeling. Instead, many human beings are in a state of mind which is just the opposite of that and is called "unhappiness" or "sadness". This has a lot to do with all that they see happening on Planet Earth, which I will tell you about in the rest of my report. It is the opposite emotion to love and this too can also affect many human beings.

Marriage

In many cases when two human beings fall in love with each other they have the need to be with each other for the rest of their time on Earth. This is so important to them that they decide to make a special commitment to each other. They will make this commitment to each other before all their family members and their friends. This is called a "marriage" and I will show you an example of one now.

Location – Galway, Ireland: a couple getting married in a hotel

"You look fantastic, darling!" It was the bride's father speaking. Before him stood his daughter on her wedding day, about to leave her dressing room at the hotel and enter the specially prepared room where fifty guests were waiting. There was a slight breeze in the air that entered the beautifully decorated room, which was awash with red and white roses. Outside it was a sunny day, perfect for the wedding of Karen and Jonathon. They had chosen to have their wedding at the Sandpiper Hotel as neither of them was particularly religious and besides you got the bridal suite thrown in, on top of the reception and marriage room.
The music started and the guests stood up and turned round to look at the bride, as several flashes went off as she started to walk down the aisle. At the same time the bride's brother was filming the whole thing on his smart phone. The bridegroom was slightly nervous, but his best man knew this and patted him lightly on his shoulder as if to say, "It's OK!". The registrar welcomed everyone and the wedding ceremony began.

This institution called "marriage" is one of the strangest of human systems. This is where two humans decide to commit everything they have to each other, supposedly for the rest of their human lives. Usually this is a pact made between the male and female of the humans. The male is given the name of "husband", whilst the female is given the name of "wife". This happens in a human ceremony called a "wedding" where friends and relatives of the husband and wife come together to watch this event. The male and the female will give each other a ring which they should wear on one of their fingers for the rest of their human lives. This is seen as a pact and is coupled with a set of words called a "vow" which they say to each other. A human elder then makes a decree that they have been married and are now "husband and wife". There is then much celebrating by the humans with a large feast laid on for everyone to enjoy.

More recently in Earth history, the ceremony of marriage has broadened out to pacts between the male and the male, or between the female and the female. Some humans don't like this or approve of this and have tried to stop this happening in various parts of the world, but it seems to have been accepted by most human beings. You might expect the animals to have a similar system but they don't. It is just the humans who do this, although many animal types do stay with their partners for their earthly lives.

Those who get married usually invite various friends and relatives to the wedding as their "guests". They all attend a celebration meal together after the marriage ceremony called a "reception", where there is a lot of singing and dancing. In many cultures on Earth the guests all give "presents" or "gifts" to the newly married couple so that they can begin their married life supported by their family and friends.

I would add that many human beings sill live together with each other as if they were married, but they don't actually go through the ceremony of marriage. They feel that they have enough trust and commitment between each other that they don't need this human institution. Also, if humans do have a wedding ceremony it costs such a lot of money that they don't want to go through with this event.

What happens if the two humans who get married decide that they do not want to stay together anymore? You may ask. Let me tell you about this.

Divorce

After some humans have been married to each other for several human years they begin to not love each other anymore. They may start to look for another partner or may separate from each other and stop the marriage from continuing Here is an event-capture which shows how this can happen.

Location – Antwerp, Belgium: inside a terraced house *

Philipp De Geyter was in bed at home. It was 11 o'clock in the morning. His wife was at work and his two children were at school. He had told his wife that he would be working from home today as he had a lot of paperwork to catch up on with his plumbing business. Yet he was actually in the throes of making love with Christine Hertmans, a single mother of two from three doors away.

They were nearing the point of orgasm and didn't hear the front door open. Philipp's wife, Amelie walked into the house and heard the groaning sounds coming from upstairs. Her heart missed a beat as she clicked as to what was going on. In an instant she was storming up the stairs, whilst Philipp and Christine heard her footsteps and immediately uncoupled.

"You bastard!" she screamed as she opened the door. Christine was desperately trying to get her clothes back on, whilst Philipp cowered under the bed sheets. Amelie jumped on the bed, her rage knowing no bounds, arms and hands reigning down blows on Philipp, who was trying to get out of the bed. "How could you betray me like this?" she shouted, a hint of despair in her voice. "And you!" she screamed, turning towards Christine who was edging out of the bedroom door. "You slut! I thought you were my neighbour. Not a husband stealer!

Amelie's heart was pounding with both anger and hatred as her twelve years of

marriage flashed by her mind's eye.

"You can get out right now!" she continued, throwing a suitcase in Philipp's direction. "I want a divorce! And I'll keep the kids and you won't ever see them again!"

Then she burst into tears and collapsed onto the bed.

The problem with this institution called marriage is that in a lot of cases the marriage pact eventually breaks down. One or both of the couples in the marriage pact decide they have had enough of this system and decide to leave the other one. The one who's left behind finds it hard to understand why the other partner did this and there are various reasons for this. Sometimes it is because one of the partners does not like making love to the other partner and so the other partner finds someone else to make love to. Sometimes one of the partners is cruel and hurtful to the other partner and he or she decides to get out of the marriage because of this.

The animals and birds and fish and insects of course don't have this system and so there is no similar equivalent form of behaviour in the animal world. On the other hand, some human couples do actually stay together for the whole of their human lives.

As each couple in a marriage pact has made a public vow of commitment to the other human it has become a legal matter. To end the marriage a special event must happen called "divorce". This is another human creation which tells everyone that the marriage has now ended. The problem with it is that it is not always fair to the two humans who are getting divorced. One of the most difficult aspects of a divorce is what is going to happen to any of the children that the two humans have created? Which parent will they live with and who will bring them up? Then there is the question of the various possessions that the two human beings have accumulated during the time that they have lived together. Who will take what possessions from the other human after the divorce has been made? These and lots of other questions cause many arguments and disagreements between the two human beings and causes the divorce to be a difficult thing in most cases. Eventually, in most cases the couples move on to new lives and forget about their former partner and find new partners that they marry. Others live in bitterness about the divorce and find it hard to forgive their former partner and forget about what has happened.

Celebrity

Many humans look up to various other humans. This means that they appreciate what they are doing with their human lives and find enjoyment in what they do. The humans call this "hero worship" as the humans who have done something special in the other human's eyes are a "hero" to them. For example, the humans are very fond of humans who are actors, or musicians, or sports people. These types of humans seem to be set apart from the other humans because they have a certain ability to do something which most other humans are not able to do. As a result of these skills, they are able to receive a lot of money for what they do. Also, because most humans know about them and take a keen interest in them they become what the humans call "famous". As a result, the ordinary humans want to be near to them and speak to them or have a photograph taken with them. Let me show you this in action.

Location - Los Angeles, USA: a film premiere

The three teenage girls peered expectantly over the barrier as flashbulbs popped incessantly towards the limousine. The chauffeur eased the shiny, black car to a stop, right in front of the red carpet and a steward opened the door. The girls immediately started screaming as one. Out stepped Romeo Watkins, the male lead for the film premiere he was attending. He was swiftly followed by his female lead, Annie Houseman. They stood smiling for the cameras, before they were ushered by their publicist towards a man with a microphone. After a brief interview, they made their way arm in arm along the red carpet towards the theatre.
"Romeo!" shouted one of the girls. But he didn't hear her as he was speaking to some fans on the other side of the red carpet. Then he swiftly turned and walked over to where the three girls were standing. They screamed louder than ever as he smiled and said, "Hi girls. How's it going?" "Romeo! We love you!" blurted out one of them. The other two held out their cell phones for him. He knew what to do and turned so that he was surrounded by, not only the three girls, but also fans on either side of them. Quickly, he took the selfie and then said, "Bye", before finding Annie further along the red carpet. After a swift wave to the crowd, he turned and went into the theatre.

Here is an example of what the humans call "celebrity". It means being known by many other humans so much that you have become famous. When you become famous you can usually receive a lot of money for what you do. This is the positive thing about being a celebrity, but there are also negative things involved as well. The person who is famous may find it difficult to go out of his or her home and walk down the street without being followed or spoken to by their "fans" or followers who want to meet them and speak to them. The result of this is that the famous person finds that they prefer to stay inside their homes rather than go out to the places. Some of these types of humans can become fearful and depressed about it all. They can also be afraid that some other humans may not like them and want to hurt them because they have become jealous of all the money they have and all the attention they are getting from the other fans.

So far in this part of my report I have shown you how humans have mainly positive relationships with each other. Now I am going to show you a very negative things that some human will do to other humans.

Murder

Location – Bogota, Colombia: a fight at a fairground *

The music from the roundabout was drowned out by the sheer number of people walking by, enjoying the sights and sounds that the fairground supplied. Antonio was walking along with his gang, The Red Cats, when he spotted the yellow and black colours of a member of a rival gang. Instantly he turned round and called to the others, "Look! There's some of the Wasp scum here! This could be interesting". He felt inside his jacket for his trusted hunting knife, a veteran of dozens of fights. He would use it if he had to, but mostly it was there as a deterrent for anyone who dared to come near him from any of the other gangs in Bogota.
People were screaming as the high swing passed above them, rotating at ever increasing speed. "Look out!, shouted Joseph,

his second in command as one of the Wasps came charging towards him, followed by about fifteen more of the gang. All hell broke loose as the two gangs began fighting. They hated each other with a vengeance and no one backed off. Fists and feet were everywhere with several gang members locked in combat on the floor where they fell. Antonio punched and kicked a Wasp in the stomach and then went for another one who was running towards him. Without thinking he grabbed his knife and held it firmly in front of him. The assailant saw it pointing right at him, but it was too late, the blade pierced him right in the middle of his stomach. Then Antonio stabbed him several times more into his torso, making sure that he wouldn't get anywhere near him. The gang member fell to the floor just as a police siren sounded and everyone started to scatter. Blood was pouring out of him and even if he had got medical help straight away, he could not have been saved.

Here you have just seen a human action known as "murder". This is when one human being or several human beings hurt another human being so much that they stop living in their bodies and "die". This is the worst action that a human being can do to another human being and it causes a big reaction. Firstly, many humans will be very hurt and upset, especially the family members and friends of this human being. Some will live the rest of their days with this event on their minds, always thinking of what this human might have done had they lived. Secondly, others will want to carry out a thing called "revenge", which means doing the same thing back to the human who "killed" the other human. This action has happened all through human history, yet many humans think that it is increasing all the time. It is a part of another human behaviour and attitude called "violence".

Many of the humans seem to be slaves to this behaviour. It happens when either a single human being or a group of human beings will hit out and hurt other human beings that they are afraid of. They might just use their fists to hit them, or their feet to kick them. Or they might use a weapon such as a knife or a gun to hurt them as in the event-capture. They might actually hurt them so much that they will badly injure the other human being or stop them from living as a human being.

105

I know that this is a hard concept to understand as on our planet we just love everyone unconditionally and do not know the human concept of fear, from which violence comes from.

Many human beings have become obsessed with violence. They like looking at violence happening in its various forms. It might be watching violent video games, or violent films which show violence in action. It might be violence in different forms on their televisions. Sometimes it is obvious and sometimes it is more subtle, such as in a detective drama where the viewer has to guess who has committed the murder. The humans watch these "entertainment" TV shows in their millions. Then there's violence on the news; wars and various conflicts taking place throughout the planet, as well as those that are local to the human. In fact, in every continent on this planet, there is violence taking place.

What is causes violence you may ask? It starts off with the human feeling of "anger" or "being angry". What makes people angry you ask? Mainly, it is not getting their own way or not being able to do what they like, and then not being able to accept this. Many humans have learnt to how to become stubborn and unyielding. If they come across someone else just as stubborn as them, or representing the law such as a policeman, they hit out, as that is the only thing left they can do. They do not consider backing down and walking away. Sometimes they might if they realise that they will get hurt or lose face or come off worse than the person they are opposing. But so many acts of violence are the result of the violent person thinking they are stronger than their opposite number and won't lose or get hurt.

Sometimes, there are the ingredients of alcohol and drugs in all this. Although alcohol is a relaxant which can make you fall asleep if you drink enough of it, most violent humans who have drunk alcohol are in the stage where they have lost any moral judgement of what is right and wrong, what is safe and dangerous, what is stupid and sensible. Alcohol dulls the senses and so makes the humans behave in a way that they wouldn't do if they were sober. I will talk more about this later.

Next I want to take you further into this subject of violence as it can also happen between countries of humans as I will show you now.

War

Location -   A country in the Middle East: civilians caught up in a war

Everywhere you looked there was rubble. Leila had become accustomed to it as she made her way through the rough path that had formed where many pairs of feet had gone before hers. She had heard that there might be a food aid delivery today and was traying to find out where this might be. All the time she had to look out for any soldiers who might suddenly appear. Sometimes they were on her side, sometimes they were the enemy.

In the distance she could hear bullets firing, but she had become indifferent to the sound. She had learnt the fine line between how far away and how near they were and didn't seem unduly bothered by them today. It was the shells and bombs you had to be more careful with. She had lost her younger brother Zayd only a month ago during an air strike when he was killed by falling rubble. Oh, how she hated this war. There was no escape for Leila. Her mother had been injured in the attack and now she couldn't walk anywhere, so Leila had to look after her and her baby sister, Ayasha, who both needed food urgently. She hoped that the people from the aid agency could help her.

As she continued her journey over the bombed out buildings she could hear the sound of gunfire increasing and her instinct told her to go back the way she had come. But she was desperate for food and needed to go on. Then, all of a sudden the sound of a missile could be heard overhead. It landed not more than a hundred yards away, followed by a very loud bang with falling masonry occurring. She needed to find safety fast, but where?

Some humans have for a long time found it difficult to be respectful to other humans. This has been between individual humans in some cases, and sometimes between large groups of humans, and even between countries. They do not like what the other says or does, and a result they become violent to the other human and want to stop them from doing whatever they don't like. In some cases, they are so violent to the other human being that they actually kill them. Whenever this happens it can lead to more and more fighting and when it grows into very large numbers of humans fighting against each other it is known as "war". In its most powerful form, it can involve several countries all fighting against each other, all hurting and killing each other.

When this happens one group of the humans will send all manner of weapons to hurt or destroy the other group of humans. They in turn will retaliate and send their weapons back to the other human group. The groups that do this are called the "army" if it takes place on land, the "navy" if it takes place at sea, or "the air force" if it takes place in the air. When there is fighting on the land the humans who are doing the fighting are called "soldiers" and these try and take over other countries if they can. The result of all this fighting is that many humans stop existing on Earth and those that they knew are left very unhappy at them leaving the planet and in some cases angry at the other side for doing this.

Also, in war there are many people called "civilians" who are not involved in the fighting who also get injured or killed, even though they haven't done anything to the other humans. Also, their homes and other buildings are often damaged or even destroyed in the war that is taking place, as you can see in this event-capture. So, it seems that war is a very negative action for the humans, yet it still takes place because they haven't learnt yet that it doesn't make things any better for the humans; only worse.

The opposite of war is called "peace". In most areas of the Earth peace exists, but it can easily change to war if the humans do not take steps to stop it from happening. Where there is peace on Earth, that is because the human society there has learnt to tolerate or understand or channel or control or turn around other people's behaviour in their particular group.

Relationships with animals

Many humans have good, positive relationships with many of the other animals existing on Planet Earth besides themselves. They have got to know them so well that they have a special relationship with them and take them into their homes to live with or near to them. Let me show you an example of this.

Pets

Location – Rotterdam, The Netherlands: the back garden of a house

The eight year old girl went into the garden shed, carrying some old newspapers, some pieces of broken up cardboard and a large refuse bag. She bent down and looked inside a rabbit hutch which was standing on a shelf right in front of her.

"Hello Alfie", she said as she opened the door. The black and white Durch rabbit came faithfully up to her and she gently picked him up. She laid him against her chest holding him underneath with her left hand. She then started stroking him with her right hand.

"it's time for a clean out Alfie" she said as Alfie looked up to her with large blue eyes. She then lifted him off her and placed him in a large cat carrier which she used to carry him in, whenever he needed to go to the vets. She shut the door and then picked up a dustpan and brush hanging by a hook in the shed on her right. Methodically she moved all the soiled newspaper, wood shavings and rabbit droppings to one end. She then brushed them into the refuse bag and tied it up with some string. Next, she sprayed some disinfectant all over the base and sides of the hutch, before laying down the cardboard followed by some newspaper sheets, and finally some wood chips.

"There. That's all nice and tidy for you once again Alfie!"
She lifted Alfie up once more and gave him some more strokes.
"Oh, you really are the best bunny rabbit in the whole wide world!" she said.
Alfie was then put back into the lovely clean hutch.

Here we have a young human female keeping a rabbit in a special box called a "hutch" which is now its home, rather than a hole under the ground where these animals usually live. This animal has in fact become what humans call a "pet" and this is a special type of relationship between a human and an animal. Humans keep all sorts of animal pets including hamsters, guinea pigs, mice, rats, gerbils and snakes. They can also keep fish in glass tanks called an "aquarium" or in a pond in their garden.

The two most popular types of animals that humans keep as pets are known as "cats" and "dogs". These two types of pets usually live inside a house with the humans as opposed to in a shed or in the garden. They become "part of the family" and are like having extra children in a household in a way. The cats are more aloof than the dogs and prefer to spend a lot of their time outside hunting or inside just sleeping. They do show affection to their human keeper, but not as much as dogs do. Dogs prefer to be near to their human owners more of the time and show more affection than cats, but they do like to go out as well for a walk with their human owners.

There are disadvantages to having a pet as well which not all humans consider before they have a pet. They need feeding and looking after and sometimes they need medical help which can all cost a lot of money. Sometimes the animals can attack other human beings and this can cause the humans a lot of problems. Do they keep the pet or do they get rid of it. Some humans actually mistreat their pets which is called being "cruel" to them. They might even just get rid of them from their homes, not caring about what happens to them. Luckily there are some kind humans who rescue these pets and take them in to their homes and find other humans to have these pets.

Apart from pets, many humans have close relationships with other animals who help them in other ways such as providing them with transport or giving them some of their products. The most popular of the first of this group of animals are "horses" who are much taller and stronger than the humans. They carry the humans on their backs or pull vehicles called "carts" to help them transport their goods about. There are also "donkeys", "camels" and "llamas" who do similar work. Then there are animals and insects who provide the humans with food such as "bees" who give their honey, "cows" who give their milk, and "chickens" who give their eggs.

Now there are some humans who use animals for sport, which means making them do things that they wouldn't normally do such as running in races as with horses and dogs. But some humans are cruel to other animals and enjoy watching this happen as I will now show you.

Cruelty to animals

As I have just mentioned some humans have learnt to be cruel with other animals who are their pets, but there are other animals that are badly treated by humans just for fun or for "sport". Here is an example.

Location - Madrid, Spain: a bull ring

The crowd of five thousand spectators – a mixture of locals and tourists – looked expectantly at the entrance to the ring. It was a hot, sunny day, with a very slight breeze and many people in the crowd waved their fans to give them some respite from the searing heat. The PA blasted out the introductory music and then the crowd all cheered as the gates opened and the procession began. First came the mounted bailiffs, followed by three matadors, the actual bull fighters, whose entrance raised a loud cheer from the crowd. Then came the toreadors on horseback, followed by the picadors carrying pikes, and finally the banderilleros on foot whose job was to place the barbed darts into the bull.
They made their way in a clockwise direction round the edge of the bull ring and then slowed down as they moved to the

centre. Then they stood and the crowd's cheering started to fade. Then there was silence as a gate at the far end of the ring opened and a bull came charging into the arena. The crowd erupted in anticipation of what they were expecting to happen. By the end of the spectacle six bulls would be dead.

Animals are hurt by humans all over the planet and this is known as "cruelty". Sometimes they do it as they are angry with the animal for doing something that they didn't want it to do. They might kick it with their feet or slap it with their hands. Sometimes they enjoy just being cruel to an animal as it makes them feel strong inside their minds. Sometimes they are cruel to an animal as it is part of a sport where the animal might be hurt and killed in some way as in this event-capture.

Some human beings like to kill animals as they enjoy chasing them around the Earth and then catching them and killing them. This is called "hunting" by the human beings and is very popular in some parts of Earth. For example, some humans like to chase foxes or hares with dogs and then let them kill them once they have caught them. Others like to watch animals fighting like dogs or chickens. Some humans like the idea of killing the animal for "fun" and actually enjoy it. The problem with this is that so many animals have been killed and not replaced that they have become "extinct" in human language, meaning that they have been completely wiped out as a type of animal or species. I will tell you more about this subject later on.

There are some human beings however, who have come to the understanding that killing animals is not the real purpose of animals existing on Earth. They have chosen to stop killing and eating animals and are trying to persuade other human beings to do the same.

Part 6

Human Organisation

Then came the churches, then came the schools,
Then came the lawyers, then came the rules......

It is now time to look at how the human beings organise themselves and live as the way they do on Planet Earth.

Time

Before I do that I must tell you about another human concept which we don't have on our planet, which dominates the humans' thinking and the way they behave. It is a concept called "time" and here is an example of it in practice.

Location – Central London, England - a man traveling on a bus to a meeting

William Musgrove was getting agitated. He was on the Number 26 bus traveling along the Strand trying to get to an important meeting near Victoria Station. He was meant to have been traveling on the Tube, but there was a problem as his train had broken down train at Temple station, so he'd got off the underground train at and caught a bus at Aldwych. In theory this should be the quickest way of getting to his meeting. He looked at his watch. It said 9.42. His meeting was due to start at 10.00 and he wasn't even near Big Ben.
He started to sweat as he became more agitated. He would be so embarrassed walking in late, yet it wasn't his fault. The bus crawled along the road, with the River Thames on his left in the distance. Then it came to yet another stop at the umpteenth set of traffic lights. It was now 9.48 as the bus continued to edge slowly along. His heart started to beat faster as he grew

*more agitated. "Why don't I take a taxi?" he thought, though
he knew that he couldn't afford the fare. "And anyway, would
a taxi be any quicker?" The bus pulled past the Houses of
Parliament and he looked at his watch yet again. It said 9.55.
If he got off here and ran, he might just make it, yet he'd be all
hot and bothered when he got there. In the end he resigned
himself to being late. After all it was circumstances beyond his
control!*

This is a typical example of a human invention which you will
find amazing. The humans call it "time", and it is what the
humans divide the daylight and the darkness into. You see
everything the humans do revolves around this thing called
time. For us, everything is just there, continually existing, but
for human beings all that they do, has to have a beginning and
an end - a sort of procession of things. They love to measure
things and divide the greater into the lesser. The concept of
time is no exception and is based on the movement of their
star across the sky when it is light and the movement of the
other stars when it is dark.

The first measurement of time that the humans use is the
movement of Planet Earth around their sun. This length of
time is called a "year", but it is not exact and every fourth year
is called a "leap year" to round up the difference. The year is
then split up into twelve smaller sections of time called
"months". These are then split up into smaller sections called
"weeks" and "days". To complicate things the months again
are not exact, with some months having thirty days in them
and other months having thirty-one days in them. There is
even one month that has just twenty eight days in it, or twenty
nine if it occurs in a Leap Year. There are seven days in one
week which is exact, but the number of weeks in a month is
not the same for every month. The days in a week have been
given the names of Sunday, Monday, Tuesday, Wednesday,
Thursday, Friday and Saturday.

Time continues to get more complicated as the days are
broken down into a group of time called "hours". There are
twenty four hours in a day which is one complete revolution of
the Earth, but the humans have split this into two parts called
"am" and "pm" or twelve hour time, roughly to do with when

there is daylight and when there is darkness. The hours are then split up further into smaller units called minutes. Yet there are more of these – sixty in one hour in fact. Finally, minutes are split up into even smaller units called "seconds" and once again there are sixty of these. Some humans have even gone as far as to split up seconds into even smaller units of time called, "micro-seconds", but most human beings cannot fathom out so small a unit of time that they don't bother going this small.

The humans have developed special contraptions to show what the time is, as they all seem to need to know about this. They are hung on the walls of their homes or workplaces or public buildings and are called "clocks". Then there are smaller contraptions called "watches" which they wear on their arms so that they can look at it many times during the day, just so they can see what time it is! If their watch isn't showing the time they thought it was, they start to get stressed or angry. This is mainly because they have set themselves certain times when things are meant to happen, such as waking up in the morning, catching a bus or train, or starting their daily work.

Next, I want to show you how just a small group of humans organize the vast majority of other humans into doing many of the things that humans do on Planet Earth.

Countries and Borders

Location – Shanghai, China: the port border control

It was 8.00am and the cruise liner had docked barely an hour ago. Already it was disgorging its passengers – a mixture of British, Americans, Spanish, Italians and other nationalities – ready to spend the day looking at the tourist hot spots in this part of China. There was an air of excitement amongst the passengers as they walked along the gangway and onto the dockside.

Ahead of them the bright red flag of the Chinese Republic flew in the breeze. Below it were two massive signs – the top half of each sign had a statement in bold Chinese script, whilst the bottom half had its English translation. It said, "Chinese Nationals to the left", and "Foreign Nationals to the right". Virtually all the passengers went to the right, where a row of cubicles stood, each with a blue shirted, Chinese immigration official sitting in them.

One by one the tourists handed over their passports and their visa forms to the immigration officials. The officials all looked intently at the tourists' faces and then at their passports, before stamping the visa twice and the passport once. They then roughly tore the visas into two parts, placing one half into a small box inside the cubicle, whilst inserting the other half into the passport and returning them to their owners. They were then allowed through the barrier and into China.

All of a sudden there was a commotion at one of the cubicles, as a female Chinese official started shouting at a male British tourist. She was waving his visa form at him and pointing to it, but he didn't have a clue as to what she was saying. There was no one about who could translate, so he looked at her with a puzzled look. Getting more irate, she rushed out of her cubicle and grabbed the visa from the woman standing directly behind him. She pointed to it, still shouting and then pointed to the ship. The British tourist got the message – he would not be allowed into China without the correct documentation.

Ever since the humans have lived on Planet Earth they have gradually spread out all over the land, constructing the buildings they call houses along with many other larger buildings. They have built villages, towns and cities which have grown to contain millions of human beings in many areas. Now some of the humans decided that they wanted to stay in one place on the Earth and not roam around, which meant that they became settled. As I mentioned earlier the humans that lived in one area began to speak with one language, whilst another set of humans in another area spoke with a different language. These different places eventually had a particular identity of their own and became known as a "country". So now on Earth there are over two hundred different countries in existence. Some countries have been in place since the early days of human existence, whilst some are quite new and have been born from other larger countries that have been divided up.

How do you know you are in one country and not another you may ask? Well, all countries on Earth have a beginning and an end where it is next to another country. The humans call this a "border". It might be a natural barrier such a range of mountains or a river: or it might be a man-made barrier such as a wall or a fence. In some cases, there is no barrier at all, apart from an imaginary line where one human foot is in one country, whilst another human foot is another country!

Sometimes the inhabitants of various countries are very keen to stop other humans from other countries coming into their country, so they set up border posts along the edge of their countries to say who should leave or come into their country. However human beings are quite ingenious in moving from one country to another and still manage to get into another country, avoiding the border posts and fences that are there.

They also have a piece of material of different colours called a "flag" flying from a tall pole and this tells you that this is where a particular country begins. If you want to get into a different country from yours, you will need a small book called a "passport" and in some cases a piece of paper called a "visa". If you don't have these you will not be allowed into a country as you have just observed.

Not only do countries have humans who speak the same language, but they also have certain practises or ways of doing things that are different to another country's way of doing that. These are called "customs" and when you get lots of these customs, it is called the "culture" of a country, that they have, or the way the country is run, as I will show you below.

Now with many millions of human Beings living in one particular country, you might wonder how each country is run. Well virtually all countries seem to be run by a small group of humans who have power over the rest of the humans in that country. I will now explain.

Human Rulers

Location – The South West of England: a stately home

The group of tourists were listening to the guide, who was showing them round the state rooms of Heathmote House, a Tudor mansion in the county of Dorset. The house and estate had belonged to the Earls of Dorchester for over four hundred years and attracted thousands of visitors every year.

The guide began, "In this room you will notice the portrait of King Charles II, who the third Earl was a close associate of".

It was painted in 1666, shortly before the Great Fire of London, by the Dutch artist, Van Leermann and is the largest surviving example of its kind".

The tourists looked up at the painting which dominated the south wall of this room. Opposite was a large, latticed window which looked out onto the rear garden of the House. A mixture of roses, dahlias and azaleas were laid out in perfect lines for several hundred yards. Beyond them a roadway stretched into the distance, reaching the boundary wall a mile away. The thirty thousand acres of land surrounding the house were grazed by sheep as had been done ever since the House was built.

The guide took the tourists into the next room where bone China vases and French pottery from the late seventeenth century were displayed. The cost of replacing just one of these would run into tens of thousands of pounds. Clearly a lot of time and money had been spent on this mansion.

"The Earls have always been close associates of the monarch throughout history whoever he or she may be. The present Earl can trace his ancestry right back to the time of William the Conqueror who gave these lands to his ancestor, Thomas de Sommerville".

The tourists listened with awe, apart from one, more cynical than the rest, who whispered to his wife, "The biggest land-grab in history!"

You may well find it astonishing that the humans have this system of one human being "ruling" over many other human beings. But this is a system which has been in existence for virtually the whole time that humans have been on Earth. The ruling humans seem to have this power over the rest of the humans in one country that makes the other human beings do what they want them to do. Yet this is not how it was in the early days of human existence on Planet Earth. Then all human beings were equal with one another just as we are on our planet. Everything around them belonged to everyone.

Then gradually on different parts of the Earth, some humans decided that they wanted to keep pieces of the Earth for themselves and so they said that a certain piece of land belonged to them and that other humans were not allowed to come onto it or use it. As most of the other humans did not object to this they took over more and more land until they became more powerful. Those who did object and try to stop this happening were stopped from their protesting by being hurt by the landowners or even killed to stop their protests. Then other humans in other parts of the planet started to copy them and eventually all the land on Earth "belonged" to small groups of humans who had taken the land for themselves.

So now on Planet Earth all the land has been divided up amongst different nations. Most countries are jealously guarded from another country taking it over by having groups of humans organised into things called "armies" who are prepared to fight to stop this happening. Before I deal with this concept, let me tell you about how the people in these countries are actually rule the rest of the humans there.

Government and Politics

Location – Westminster Palace, London - the House of Commons

"Will the honourable member please explain what he means when he says that tax increases by the government are in the best interests of everyone'?"

Immediately, the person who asked the question sat down and a tall man opposite him, also in a suit, just stood up to speak.

"My party has decided that that due to your party's incompetence in running this country when you were in power, that we have been left with no alternative but to pick up the pieces by increasing the basic rate of tax to pay for your mistakes."
Cheers went up from his side of the Commons as the honourable member sat down.
"Order! Order!" shouted the Speaker of the House, situated right in the middle of the two sides.
The first man to speak got up once more and replied, "It seems to me that the honourable member must have got his facts wrong, because when we were the government of this country, we ran this country to a strict budget and didn't overspend!" Immediately derisive laughter sprang out from opposite him, whilst behind him more cheers went up.
"Order! Order!" shouted the speaker once again.............

At one time in the past on Planet Earth all men were equal. Those who were older and had lived longer became well-respected as the source of wisdom and gave guidance about what to do in a particular situation. The "elders" as they were known would listen to and give their advice, which was acted upon for the best interests of each community. Gradually different individuals thought that they knew better than the elders and so persuaded other humans to follow them and they gradually got more power from the other humans and took it for themselves. They started telling other people what to do and how to live. Foolishly the other people did what these people told them to do, partly out of respect. partly out of fear and partly because they couldn't make decisions for themselves. This is the origin of people in control of other human beings, so that today we have dictators, royal families and governments who all make the decisions for the rest of the people.
In the old way of ruling the people, there was one person called a "king" or a "queen" or a "chief" who held absolute power and the rest of the humans had to do what he or she said. When he or she died, his son or daughter would take over as the ruler of the country and the whole system would continue as if nothing had happened. Nowadays on Planet

Earth there are not that many of these types of rulers in place as little by little the majority of the humans in some countries took back the power that their ancestors had given away. They had decided that they didn't want to be ruled by just one human being alone, especially as these rulers seemed to keep all the best food and the buildings and the material things for themselves. The majority of the people were living with only the basic human necessities and food, and were in effect, "slaves", which means that they had to do everything that the ruler told them to do.

Little by little the anger and sense of injustice within them built up and they decided that they didn't want to be ruled by their rulers anymore and a great outpouring of anger against their rulers took place. The humans called these events "revolutions" and as a result of them the way their countries were ruled changed. There are some countries on the planet that are still rules in this way where the humans have to do as they are told and they are not allowed to complain or protest.

One different system that came in was called "democracy" which you can see here in action. In it the wishes of the people are listened to and argued about until an agreement is reached. This is when the majority of the people agree that they want something to happen. Of course, all the people of one country can't all decide at the same time that they want something to happen, so they choose a human called a "politician" to make the decisions on their behalf. They choose these politicians by voting for them in elections where the one with the most votes is chosen. In many countries these politicians become the "government" and it is they who decided on the way that the country is governed.

Another system of government which they have in some countries is called "communism" and this is different in that all the people are meant to share the country's wealth and resources as one. It sounds similar to the way we do things on our planet, but in reality it is no different than the monarch ruled system. This is because those at the top of the government invariably take all the best food and homes and possessions for themselves.

Religion

Scene – Lisbon, Portugal: inside a church

The young woman entered the church as sunlight started to penetrate the stained glass windows at the north end of the church. It was only 8 o'clock in the morning, yet the young woman felt the need to be there. As she walked past the main aisle of the church, which led to the high altar, she bent her knee and crossed herself. She then proceeded towards a table, full of small candles. Two or three were alight and she added another, again crossing herself as she placed her candle amongst the others.

Walking back towards the central aisle, she then walked up it a little, going through the same motions of kneeling and crossing herself, before she found a seat in the long wooden pews. She knelt and crossed herself again, before sitting in silent prayer to the god she believed in for help with her problem.

After ten minutes she got up and walked round to the left side of the church, where a large and heavily decorated metal framed box stood. She opened a curtain and went into the cubicle. She sat down and drew the curtain across, before she tapped lightly onto a piece of wood facing her. Within seconds the wood slid to the right and a metal grill appeared.

"Bless you my child" said a man's deep voice the other side of it. "Are you ready to make your confession?" "Yes Father," she replied. "I have sinned………"

When humans first lived on Earth they were fully connected with the Source and all their senses were at one with the world and the universe they lived in. Gradually as they moved around the Earth and explored all that it contained their connection with the Source gradually glue grew weaker. Until one day their connection was broken. This meant that in practice humans didn't feel connected to the Source and from that date onward they tried to get back to the original connection they had. They thought of the Source as being up in the sky, or up in the mountains away from them on the ground. Instead of having love for the Source and everything in the world they began to have fear. They feared that if they didn't do something to make the Source happy they would be in danger of not eating, or not having shelter, or not being at peace with other humans.

This lead to some humans exploiting that fear and saying that they were the intermediary between the Source and the humans. If they obeyed certain rules that they made, or did certain rituals, or gave some of their possessions, or food or money to these intermediaries they would be able to access the Source through them. Many humans believed and trusted these humans and still do today, not realising that the Source was inside them already as they were part of the Source and didn't need to do what these intermediaries said. Those who did as the intermediaries said became part of what is known as a "religion" and there are many on the planet at this time.

All human religions have their own set of rules which are mainly concerned with how an individual human being should live its life. The human beings who follow a religion are not allowed or able to think for themselves or make up their own minds about the way they should live. Instead, they have to obey the laws that they made up. What sort of laws you may ask? Well, it could be about what sort of clothes you wear, such as clothes which cover different parts of the human body: or what sort of food you can eat, such as not eating animal meat, or only certain kinds of animal meat. They could be about being at a religious building at a certain time during the week, or saying a certain prayer to the Source, or moving the body in a certain way at a certain time of the day. If they don't obey these laws they will be thrown out of that religion, or worse still the Source will reject them completely and they will be sent to a place they call "hell".

Although many humans still follow these religions and obey these laws, there are many other humans who have rejected these religions or religious beliefs. Instead, they are thinking for themselves and realising that they are already part of the Source and can do whatever they like, providing they don't hurt other humans or creatures on the Earth.

Education

Scene – Singapore: a primary school classroom

The class of nine and ten year olds sat silently by their desks which were arranged in neat little rows of five columns. They all stood up in rapt attention as their teacher came into the classroom. Outside traffic buzzed past with cars, lorries and bicycles all vying for a piece of the tarmac so that they could get to their destination.
"Good morning class 6" said the teacher, Mr. Choon Seng.
"Good morning Sir" replied Class 6 in unison.
"Today we are going to practise for your Mathematics exam which you will be taking in three weeks' time". With that he started to place face down a Maths practice paper on each desk. As soon as he had finished, he looked at his watch, before announcing to the class, "You have exactly thirty minutes to attempt this Maths paper. You may turn over and begin".
With that each child turned over the paper and began the practice test".

One of the main purposes for humans on Planet Earth is experiencing a process called "learning" which involves taking in information about a whole host of different events and subjects. Learning is designed to take place all through the humans' lifetime on Earth, yet many humans have closed their minds to learning once they become adult humans and so do not progress much in their human experience. Part of the reason for this is the fact that many human beings are subject to a human version of learning when they are children called "education". With this system the humans are made to attend a building in their village or town called a "school". They have to attend school for several years until they become adults and although at first they are quite happy to do this, as they become older they start to resist going to school.
This can be due to a number of different reasons. The main one is that school learning for many children has been about topics which are not about their everyday human existences. Instead, they are made to learn about abstract subjects which

have no relevance to their human lives. This is backed up by having to have "tests" or "exams". These are when the child has to remember all that he or she has learnt by answering different questions or writing about a certain subject. If they remember most things or answer the questions correctly they will be told they have "passed " their exam. But if they don't do this they will be told that they have "failed" their exam and will have to take their exam again or be labelled as a failure.

All this has a negative effect on children who see school as a big pressure on their lives, rather than as a preparation for their future lives. This continues into their adult human lives where they are "educated" in other ways as you will see.

Rules and regulations

Education is just one part of the many systems that human beings have invented. It is seen as a way of preparing the young human beings for when they become adults. Just as children are told to obey rules or they will be punished, so it is with the adult human beings as well. These are known as rules and regulations. Let me show you how this works with the adult humans.

Location – Aalborg, Denmark: a health and safety inspection at an industrial unit.

The bespectacled man was carrying a clip board and pen in his right hand, whilst in his left hand he held a tape measure. In his pocket was a large torch which he would shine into every nook and cranny in the hope of finding something that wasn't quite right. If the company wasn't following the health and safety rules to the letter, he had the power to shut down the unit until all the wrongs had been righted. The foreman who was showing the inspector around knew this and was very nervous.

"Right! Let's start with the store room", said the inspector in a voice full of authority.

"If you'll follow me", said the foreman. "It's just at the far end of the unit".

The inspector followed the foreman along a corridor, all the time observing every detail that he could see.

The foreman came to the store room and got out a bunch of keys. He chose the correct one and unlocked the door. It was pitch black and he leant inside and switched on the light. Straightaway the lights illuminated the room and the inspector went inside, looking all around him as he moved forward. The foreman was now starting the sweat with fear. The inspector didn't notice him, but instead spotted some dirty rags on the floor. He got out his clipboard and wrote down some words.

After some minutes where he lifted various containers and bent down to see what was on the floor, he announced, "Right. I've seen enough here. Let's move onto your office. I want to look at your records".

The foreman became more nervous and more sweaty as he led the way. Was he going to mess things up. He hoped the records were up to date, but you never knew.

Most of the humans live on Planet Earth under a system which is built on the basis of "rules and regulations". These rules are types of commands created by just one human being in some cases, or by a small group of human beings in other cases. The humans are then expected to "obey" these rules which tell them how to live their lives on Earth in various ways. These rules have been invented to try and help control different aspects of human behaviour. Sometimes this is for the good of all humans, and sometimes this is for the benefit of just one human being who is in charge of their lives.

Whilst most humans accept these rules and obey them, there are some humans who do not accept them and do not do what the rules say. In other words, they "break the rules". If they do this and those with the power over them find out they can be "punished" which means that they will have to have something done to them to restore the balance of things.

There are two groups of humans who break these rules. The first group break these rules as they do not accept the rules of the human who is ruling over them, perhaps because this human is hurting many of the humans in their country. They see this as affecting their basic "human rights", which are various unwritten rules which all human beings should have during their time on Earth.

The second group go by the name of "criminals" who you will find out about now.

Crime and criminals

There are some human beings who do not like having to obey rules and regulations, especially when it comes to obeying more major rules called "laws", which are to do with how you should behave. These humans are doing whatever they chose, even if they hurt another human being in the process. For instance, this can be taking things from another human being, "theft" or destroying some object that another human has created, "vandalism", or actually hurting another human being so that they can get what they want, "assault". This "breaking of the law" is called "crime" by the humans and the humans who cause crime are known by the word, "criminals" and I will show you what this means below.

Location: New York City, USA - a police car chase

The two teenagers rushed out of the back of the suburban house that they had just broken into. They carried a suitcase filled with their haul including watches, a computer, a camera, and a variety of jewellery. The older one carried a set of car keys which he knew would be belong to the saloon on the driveway. He pressed the key hob and opened the driver's side door and got in as his companion got in on the other side. He started the engine and they were away.

Ten minutes later he looked in the rear view mirror and saw the blue flashing lights of a cop car. Immediately he pushed the throttle hard and sped away, but the police car came after him and a chase had begun.

"Left, left, left!" shouted the NYPD officer from his passenger seat as the police car he was in veered sharply to the left into the side street. His left hand held the radio whilst his right hand gripped the handle above the window. To the left his co-

officer held onto the car's steering wheel tightly, his eyes fixed on the stolen cabriolet several yards ahead.
The fifteen year old driver of the stolen car was both scared and excited at the same time.
"Faster you jerk!" urged his companion, who was high on adrenaline. "They won't get us if you keep your foot down!"
The car swerved suddenly as it went over a pot hole. The driver held the steering wheel tighter and kept his foot down. A car started to pull out from a side street on the left so he braked hard and steered the car to the right, but a car was coming the other way straight at him. Meanwhile the chasing police car was closing in on him and he knew he was trapped. He tried to go on the sidewalk, but there was a fire hydrant in the way and the car crashed hard into it, shooting water all over the street. He was stunned but managed to open the door and get out....straight into a police officer pointing a pistol at him.

You may be shocked to hear that there are some humans who organise themselves into groups to steal from other humans or hurt other humans. These criminals have their main focus in life as committing crime. There are all sorts of crimes, with murder and rape being the worst crimes, and others like theft, forgery, fraud and violence against an individual human being some of the others. In fact, some of these humans are so angry within themselves that they don't reason that they are hurting other humans when they commit these crimes.
Crime then is what happens when one human being does something to another human being which the majority of humans don't want to happen. Over a long period of Earth time different actions of the humans have come to be classed by the majority as "wrong" or "against the law". When I say "the law" I am referring to laws or rules which have been devised by some humans who think that other humans must behave in this particular way. When a human doesn't behave in that particular way then he or she has "committed a crime", as most humans don't want this one human to do this. As a result of committing this crime, the other humans have said that this person must undergo some sort of retribution or punishment, as a type of karma to restore the balance and

harmony. I will show you what can happen at the end of this part of my report.

The root of most crime is the thought that these humans don't have enough of that thing I mentioned earlier called money. They think that if they had more of this money then their lives would be happier and more fulfilled. So, they try whatever they can to get more of this money, even if it means hurting another human being either physically or mentally. Many crimes are the result of some humans not sharing the amount of money that they had. So, some humans have lots of money and others have very little money. This inequality leads to emotions such as jealousy, envy and anger and in the end leads to some humans committing these crimes.

There are some humans who are organised in groups whose sole purpose is to stop and catch these criminals. They are known as the "police" and they operate in every part of the Earth. When they catch a criminal they "arrest" them and many of them are spending their time moving around different areas looking out for criminals so that they can catch them. Other groups of humans known as "detectives" spend their time trying to "solve" or sort out a crime and work out which human criminal may have committed the crime.

So, what happens if a criminal is caught ? A system called "justice" is in place to deal with the criminal and I will show you an example of this in action.

Justice

Location – London, England: Court Number 6 at the Old Bailey

Court Number 6 at the Central Criminal Court was packed. In the public gallery the accused's family sat on one side and the victim's family, outnumbering the first family by three to one, were on the other side. Separating them were three policemen as well as two court officials, ready for any possible altercations once the verdict was read out. Below them in the court room were several different groups all connected with the case including the twelve person jury, members of the press, the stenographers, and the two legal teams including the barristers. Both sets of barristers, who represented the accused or defendant on one side and the prosecution on the other, all wore black gowns over their suits. On their heads were funny little wigs tied up at the back with white bows.

Finally in the dock was the accused, twenty eight old Wayne Morris, wearing a brown suit with matching brown tie and white shirt. He was constantly looking down to the ground as if irritated by an insect crawling around his feet. Once in a while he would look up to the public gallery and give a quick nod to his mother, who had been in court every day since the four week trial had begun. Now it was the final day. The prosecution and the defence had called their witnesses and summed up their cases in final speeches to the jury. The judge had also summed up the case and directed the jury on the law. The jury had been out for two days deliberating over whether the accused was guilty or not guilty and now they had reached their verdict.

The clerk of the court stood up and said, "All rise!". Everyone in the court immediately stood and then a door opened at the back of it and then the judge, Mr Justice John Stewart, entered the courtroom. He was wearing a scarlet robe with fur facings and on his head was a similar size wig to the barristers.

"All sit!" ordered the clerk of the court and everybody obeyed, apart from the defendant who had been told to stand.

The judge then sat down and spoke to defendant directly,

"Wayne Gary Morris", you have been brought before this court on the very serious charge of murder. The jury has reached their verdict. Now it is time to hear this verdict.

"Will the foreman of the jury please stand" said the clerk of the court.

A woman with jet black hair in her fifties stood up nervously and looked at the judge.

"Madam foreman of the jury", the clerk said, "How do you find the defendant on the count of murder?"

She cleared her throat and spoke as clearly as she could,

"Not guilty", she said.

The clerk continued "And is that the verdict of you all?".

"Yes" replied the foreman.
Immediately a loud, raucous cheer went up in the public
gallery from the defendant's family. At the same time several
moans and cries of anguish came from the other side of the
public gallery. Wayne Morris himself fell to the floor of the
dock and started to cry tears of relief.
"Silence!" shouted the Judge, but it was to no avail. Wayne
Morris had been found not guilty on the sole count of murder
and that was that.

In this event-capture you can see the system of justice in
action. When a human has been caught doing something
against the law and is caught by the law enforcers this human
is allowed in most places on Earth to have what is known as a
"trial". This is what is happening in the event-capture and is
where the human has to explain what he or she has or has not
done. There are humans in the court room called "lawyers" or
"barristers" who argue that he is guilty of the crime or not
guilty of the crime. Then in many countries there is a group of
humans called a "jury" who then decide which of these two
options is the correct "verdict". Over everyone is the leader of
the court called a "judge" who decides whether he or she
should go to prison if it is a guilty verdict.
In less important cases the judge is called a "magistrate". In
some places they do not have a jury and it is just the judge
who decides if the human is guilty or not. The whole process
is known as "justice" and most humans see this as the best
way of sorting this out.
Sometimes a trial is not about a individual human, but instead
it is about a group of humans known as an organization. One
problem with justice is that it is sometimes not the correct
verdict and the person who is not guilty or "innocent" of a
crime and is found to be "guilty". So, he or she could be sent
to prison even though they haven't committed a crime. The
other option could also happen when a guilty human is found
"not guilty" and is set free. Sometimes the judge might be
bribed, or feel sorry for someone, so it is not completely
failsafe.
Justice is one of the most important things to humans as they
like to have things balanced in their lives. Outside of a

country's justice system, humans still practise their own form of justice from time to time. For instance, if a human male hits another human male in the face, the human who was hit will usually hit the other human back in his face. This is called" revenge" or "getting even". This behaviour is important to most humans as they seem to have this in-built mechanism which makes them react in the same way that the person who hits them does. Some humans however do not want to get revenge or get even with someone who may have hurt them in some way. Instead, they use an action called "forgiveness" where they decide not to react in the same way as the person who hurt them. They feel that this is a better way to live and so leave things to settle down. That is not to say that they always do nothing, as they might speak to the other human and say their side of the story and try and get that person to see what they have done wrong.

Now If a criminal person is found guilty in a court, as a punishment they are sometimes sent to a human building called a "prison". This is what a prison is like.

Prisons

Location – Mexico City, Mexico: inside a prison

Antonio Mendez was serving an eight year jail term for drug trafficking. He was two years into his sentence and he was hating it. Not only did he miss his girlfriend, who might well have left him by now, but the conditions were atrocious. He was covered in sores from the bed bugs and fleas that he shared his prison cell with. He hated the smells that followed him everywhere – from the damp of his cell to the urine that came from the latrines and showers. From the rotten cabbage smell at meal times to the sweaty odour from all the testosterone crazed prisoners, most of whom he tried to avoid. One thing he couldn't avoid though were the guards, whose routine would be to wake him up at 6.00am every day, banging on his cell door. If he was lucky they wouldn't beat him with their steel batons. Then after washing and toileting he would join the long line for breakfast in the prison canteen. This time you had to avoid the menacing stares of the chief prisoners, who might summon you over to carry out a favour for them if they felt like it. There was always this underlining feeling of fear amongst most inmates as they knew beatings and even rape could happen at a moment's notice. How he hated it here.

Punishment for committing crimes can take lots of different forms. Over the years humans have devised all sorts of punishments for the lawbreakers ranging from putting another human to death as the most extreme, through to locking them up in a jail or prison for a certain amount of time, or just making them give another person some of their money or possessions.

The jail option involves putting the human into a building that he is not allowed to leave until a certain amount of time has passed. The windows all have bars on them and the doors are all locked and the walls are all very high, so that he could not leave or "escape" if he wanted to. Once he has "served his time" he will be let out of the prison and then must try and not commit any more crimes, or he will be put back in the prison again. Several humans find being in prison very hard to take and make sure that they do not commit any more crimes once they are set free. Other humans seem to go into prison, get set free and then come back to prison time and again until they eventually die there.

These then are some of the most important ways in which the humans organise themselves. In the next part of my report, I will tell you about how the humans have created various things which are mostly pleasant and helpful to other humans.

Part 7

Human Creativity

Music is the healing force of the world,
It's understood by every man, woman, boy and girl

Human Creativity

One of the things about humans compared to other creatures is that they are able to "create". This means being able to bring into existence something which wasn't originally physically there. They will first have a concept called an "idea", which starts off in their brain and then this grows stronger until they start to create it with their hands, guided by what their brain is telling them. Whilst the birds and animals on Earth are able to create small things, like a home, they are unlike humans, as they cannot create large and complicated things, other than these basic things. For instance, many humans have the ability to paint beautiful pictures, or compose wonderful music - but more of that later. Animals of course cannot do these things.

From earliest childhood right through to their final years, humans create. Let's not forget that their creativity can be stifled by the thing known as "work" or by the human activity called "worrying". But all humans are capable of creating great things whether it is art, music, buildings or clothes. In this section of my report, I will tell you about several different types of creativity that the humans have evolved to do. Most of them are positive in nature, but a few are negative.

Art

Let us start by looking at the creative action called "Art" by the humans. Art is concerned with the human expressing him or herself through different forms such as painting or drawing.

Location – Paris, France: a gallery inside the Louvre Museum

Louise and Gary were excited. Here they were on honeymoon in Paris and thousands of miles away from their American home. They had seen most of the sights of the city including the Eiffel Tower, Sacre Coeur, Napoleon's Tomb and Notre Dame. Now it was the final day of their holiday and they just had to visit the Louvre.

They had queued patiently for over fifty minutes and now they were being let into what was perhaps the most famous room in the museum. Earlier they had seen so many different paintings from the most famous artists including Rembrandt, Turner, and Renoir. Now they were about to see the ultimate painting, which would make their trip worthwhile, the famous Mona Lisa by Leonardo Da Vinci. The eyes of the female in the world famous painting seemed to follow them as they approached it. They could hear gasps of awe from some Japanese tourists in front of them. Louise couldn't help herself as she let out a "Wow!" and was drawn ever closer to that iconic work of art. Gary too was impressed, though he kept his thoughts to himself.

They wished that they could take a photo or two, but the security guards were watching everyone like hawks. In fact, they weren't allowed to linger too long as the demand to see this painting was immense. Reluctantly they had to move away to make way for the next batch of tourists, but at least they had seen perhaps the most famous painting in the world and that was an achievement to be proud of.

One of the creative activities of humans which sets them apart from the animals is that they are able to create with their hands and fingers pictures which imitate the real life on Earth that the Source first created. Through the use of their fingers holding pens, pencils, crayons, brushes and paints, humans have always created Art. This might have been pictures and paintings on the walls of caves in the early days. Then through time this skill has developed into highly complicated and intricate pictures and patterns which they have placed onto paper or canvas. Other humans looking at these art works have then found these pictures or paintings pleasing and inspirational to them.

The humans who have this ability to create pictures and paintings create what humans call "masterpieces" or "works of art". These pictures and paintings have hung in people's homes and palaces for many years. Some humans like collecting these pictures and put them together in a building called an "art gallery" where other humans can go and look at them. Some humans like the paintings so much, that they hand over large amounts of money to own them.

The ability to create pictures and paintings is in all humans. As children, the humans do create simple pictures, but as they grow older most humans lose this ability and do not try and create pictures any more. In fact, only a small number of humans continue to do this. Those humans who have this ability or skill to create pictures, make them look so much like the real thing they are copying, that you would think the Source had done it!

So far, I have shown you the unique human activity of Art, but some human beings have taken this activity a step further and drawn their art forms on their own bodies. This practice has been going on for thousands of Earth years, but in the present time it has gained momentum once again. To make the colours remain on the human flesh and not get washed away, the humans have to pierce the skin of their bodies with a needle and insert different colours. Eventually a pattern or picture emerges which the human being must carry on its body for the rest of the time that it stays on Earth. At first human beings created their art forms just on their arms and on their torsos, but in recent times every part of the human body is now capable of being covered with this art form.

Also related to this activity is a similar activity of piercing the human flesh to place small metal objects into holes on the human flesh. This again involves the reaction in the human body called "pain" so that a hole can be made in the human flesh. At first the human beings pierced their ears to put in an object called "earrings". Now this activity has expanded to include all parts of the human face such as the eye brows, lips and tongue as well as the reproductive parts of the human body, both male and female.

Photography

The humans have now reached the stage in their development where they have developed the skill to capture a moment of Earth time in a small box. This box is called a "camera" and can capture a moment which is either still or moving. A still capture is called a "photograph", whilst a moving capture is called a "film" or "movie". Let us look at the still capture part first.

Location   Monte Carlo, Monaco: A group of people and paparazzi waiting for the arrival of a princess

Behind the crash barrier stood a veritable arsenal of paparazzi and ordinary people all waiting expectantly. The photographers had the very best cameras available, all with telephoto lenses, capable of capturing the minutest detail of anything passing within inches of them. Some of them had bought along small step ladders so they could add some height to their shots, as well as avoid the heads of the members of the public all waiting to get a glimpse of the princess as she passed by.
Luckily, the rain had been and gone and the sun was once again shining high in the sky. This could mean problems for the paparazzi, as too much sunlight could ruin their shots, in spite of their filters. They were all hoping to get the perfect shot of the princess, as that could mean a large payment from the nationals who would pay handsomely for the right picture. Although they weren't that keen on the public being amongst them, it did have its positives. They could act as "bait" by speaking to the princess and her entourage, giving them the chance to get a still photo with time to get several shots as they spoke.
"They're here!" shouted someone at the front and immediately everyone raised their cameras. The black car stopped a few feet away from where everyone was standing.

Security men looked around suspiciously at the crowd and an equerry opened the door nearest to where she was sitting. Flashes went off in a fury as the princess stepped out of the car. A huge cheer came from the crowd as the princess shook hands with various local dignitaries lined up to greet her. Then she walked towards the crowd and started speaking to some of the crowd. More flashes went off and the paparazzi got their shots. Less than five minutes later she was gone.

In this event-capture you can see that those humans carrying the cameras have a desire to capture a moment in time. They want to remember this day for the rest of their lives – the day I saw a princess. It will be a lasting memory created in their lives. They will be able to show the photographs they captured of the famous person and show other family members or their friends that special moment in time. Many years from now they will look back at the photographs they took this day and remember those moments with gladness.

Sometimes when they look at other photographs, perhaps of their friends or family members they will become sad because the people in the photograph which they are looking at will no longer be on the Earth plane and be no longer in their lives. Photographs are a useful way for the human beings to remember special days or events in their lives.

The other group of humans in the event-capture are taking photographs of the princess for different reasons. They aren't interested in creating memories from the photographs they take. Instead, they are more concerned with creating money from the photographs that they take. This is because they will be able to sell the photographs for money to another set of humans. The better the photograph they take, the more likely they will be able to sell it to a newspaper or magazine, who will then use it to illustrate an article or news item. Sometimes these professional photographers will sell photographs of a famous person to a newspaper or a magazine which will get the famous person into trouble with someone else, who do not like what is happening in the photograph. It might be a close relative or friend who gets hurt emotionally by what they see in the photograph. Or it might be the police who can see that the person is "breaking the law" and doing something that needs to have a punishment.

Let us not forget that there are plenty of photographs taken by the humans which are art in themselves such as the various beautiful things on Planet Earth. It could be the beauty of the mountains or lakes or the sea. Or it could be some wildlife such as animals or birds. Or nature such as flowers or trees, or mountains and lakes. Like paintings some photographs can be hung on walls in homes and galleries for humans to look at. Now it is time to look at how moving pictures work.

Moving Pictures

As well as having learnt to capture a single moment in time, the humans have also learnt to go to the next stage and that is to capture a moving image. Let me show you.

Location – Bucharest, Romania : a horror film is showing in a cinema

A torchlight was shining across the room of the deserted house. It was held by a fifteen year old girl who had entered the house, searching for her lost dog. It had run off after it was spooked by a loud bang. So she had no alternative but to go after it, even though the house was boarded up, whilst undergoing repairs. Suddenly the teenage girl screamed in terror as a grotesque clown face appeared in front of her. The audience in the cinema also gasped in shock at the sight of the clown. Some even jumped in their seats. The effect was intensified by the fact that the audience were wearing special 3D glasses, so the face of the clown seemed as if it was coming straight out of the screen, right at them.

The clown carried a large knife in his right hand and started to chase the girl round the room. She continued screaming as she searched frantically for the door and a possible escape. The clown raised his right hand with the blade of the knife glistening in the torchlight. Several people in the cinema actually started to scream, whilst others held the hands over their faces, not daring to look.

The girl grabbed at the door handle and swung it open. The force of the door opening, hit the clown full on in his face and he dropped the knife, shouting out a curse as blood began to trickle from his nose. The girl meanwhile had run down the stairs and across the hallway to the window, where she had entered the house. She climbed through the window and into the cold night air. She was safe. The audience let out a collective sigh, relieved that she had come to no harm.

These 'moving pictures' are known as "films" or "movies" by the humans. Films can show everyday human life as it happens in real terms, or they can show made up events called "plays" which I will tell about below. Humans enjoy watching these different forms which are made possible by the technology of the camera capturing the scene before it. Only with films the camera is able to capture the movement of the human and not just one still moment from its life. Watching a film or movie as in the above event-capture can cause all sorts of reactions in the humans watching them. They can show fear as in this event-capture, or they can exhibit laughter as they find the subject matter amusing or "funny". Or some films can make the humans watching them angry as they can see something in their world which needs altering as other humans are suffering in some sort of way.

Some films can show just drawings which have been brought to life through thousands of pictures drawn almost the same, but with a slight difference in each case. These are known as " cartoons" and are particularly enjoyed by the younger humans. In fact, human technology has developed so much that nowadays the humans do not have to spend a lot of time drawing these pictures as their computers will do it for them.

The one problem with the moving pictures that humans create is that some humans can become what is known as "addicted" to watching certain types of films. This means that they find it very hard to stop themselves from watching them, however hard they try not to. They keep getting drawn back to them and it starts affecting their health, or their relationships with other humans. The sort of films that can become addictive to some humans include the ones that show violence between humans or sexual actions. These humans sometimes end up needing extra help from other humans to break free from their addictions. But humans don't just get addicted to watching certain types of films, they can be addicted to all sorts of things which you will see later in my report.

Theatre/plays/drama

Closely connected with the creative art of moving pictures, a play or a drama is another creation of human beings. Usually, it is performed "live" as it happens before an audience in a theatre. Let me show you an example.

Location – Stratford-upon-Avon, England: a Shakespearean play being performed on stage

People had travelled from all over the world to be here. They had come from as far afield as the USA, Japan, China, South Africa and Australia to witness one of William Shakespeare's most well-known plays being performed in a theatre that was built in the town where he had once lived and where the play would have been performed many times over the years.
"To be, or not to be. That is the question." The famous words written in bold white letters had greeted the audience as they entered the building. Many had bought souvenir booklets and other memorabilia from the stall selling such souvenirs. Others had partaken of a quick drink or two before they had come into the theatre with various lights shining onto the stage.
Many just sat taking it all in – the sense of history, the energy of the place and most of all the connection with the great bard himself. There was a feeling of anticipation all around the theatre as the audience waited for the play to begin.
Once the audience was all seated and various safety and other announcements had been made, the lights dimmed and there was a palpable sense of awe from everyone.
A solitary light went on and the stage could be just about seen, with the silhouette of a castle as a backdrop.
"Who's there?" boomed a male voice from one end of the stage.

As the actor spoke these words there was a huge wave of recognition from the audience. "Hamlet" was underway.

Another creative aspect of human beings is their ability to pretend that they are another person. In this scenario a group of human beings called "actors" come together to "act" or pretend that they are living the life of a different human being. This is called a "play" and will have been created by one human being who has decided how this group of human beings will speak and behave. For some reason that you will find difficult to understand human beings actually enjoy going to a building called a "theatre" and sitting down to watch the actors perform their play. The actors will be higher up from the audience on a specially build platform called a "stage". Just like a moving picture film they enjoy the aspect of forgetting their normal daily lives and like the idea of seeing what other humans are doing in their lives, even if it is not exactly true or real.

Plays can have all sorts of stories where the human emotions of greed, anger, jealousy, lust and hatred are shown in the actions of the actors. These emotions are negative human emotions, but the play can also show the opposite of these, such as friendship, joy, peace, self-sacrifice and love. You will learn all about these emotions in the part of my report which looks at human feelings.

Whilst this event-capture shows a play or "drama" being performed inside a theatre, there are other mediums where plays are performed as in a moving picture. Another one is on the medium known as "television", of which I have already shown you an example in a different part of my report.

Now I will move onto a completely different art form which is not so much concerned with using the eyes, but more concerned with speaking with the mouth and listening with the ears.

Comedy and Laughter

Another way which humans use their creativity is by putting together words in a sentence in such a way that the humans find what they are saying is "funny". This is when the humans use their vocal chords to bring forth a sound called "laughter". This means that humans are in a happy frame of mind and are not concerned about anything else. Let me show you this in action.

Location – Buenos Aries, Argentina: inside a comedy club

"I used to run a dating service for chickens, but I found it hard to make hen's meet!" said the comedian.
Everyone burst into laughter and clapped. Some even cheered and whistled. The comedian was on good form tonight and the crowd were loving the jokes he told.
He tried a new one on the audience.
"Police arrested two teenagers yesterday", he said. "One was drinking battery acid and the other one was eating fireworks". He paused for effect and then delivered the punchline. "They charged one – and let the other one off!"
The crowd in the comedy club were in hysterics. They couldn't stop laughing at whatever the comedian said. Much of his material rang a bell with them in their everyday lives. Some of the women in the audience had to wipe tears from their eyes as they laughed so much.
"What does a storm cloud wear under its raincoat?" he continued.
Again, he waited ever so slightly for the question to sink in. "Thunderwear!"
This time he shouted the punchline for extra effect. It garnered even more laughter and applause. He was having a good day. This audience loved him and shared his sense of humour.
"Ladies and gentlemen. You've been a terrific audience tonight", he said. "Here's one to be leaving you with…..
I was having dinner with the world chess champion the other night and the table had a check tablecloth on it. It took him an hour to pass me the salt!".

More laughter and applause. Some even stood up to hail the comedian. He'd had a successful night.

From the above event-capture you can see that the humans find certain things funny and when they feel that something is funny they "laugh" at it. This is showing that the humans have a side to their mind which is known as having "a sense of humour". This is quite difficult to explain as we do not have this type of behaviour on our planet as we are permanently in a state of happiness or bliss. The humans use this sense of humour to counteract negative feelings they have about the life they are living. When a person puts together a series of sentences that are funny this is known as a "joke". The person who tells these jokes is known as a "comedian" and they are very popular with humans as they make them laugh and so help them to become happier in their lives as you have just seen above.

To create jokes as they do is quite a skilled activity and the comedian or the human who writes jokes for him or her has to be able to think of something that is funny in the first place. Sometimes they find something that is funny from the way other humans say or do something. Something they find something funny by using a single word, or just a few words which will be said at the end of the joke. The way the comedian says the joke is also important as if it is not said in the right way, the other humans might not laugh when the joke is said. Like sports many hundreds and thousands of people come to watch a comedian as they find the idea of laughing at something a way of making themselves happier.

Now it is time to tell you about a completely different creative art that the humans have created. This time it involves sounds and vibrations.

Music

Another of the creative arts that humans have developed is the art form known as "music". This is one of the most pleasurable of human activities as it has the effect of making the humans happy and contented. This is something that is not visible, but rather is an audible event that enters the human brain through the ears. It will be difficult for you to grasp this concept as we have nothing like it on our planet. There are all sorts of different music that humans like to listen to and I will show you an example of one type of music.

Location – Salzburg, Austria: a classical concert performance

The conductor entered the concert hall and moved to the rostrum as the audience applauded. He turned to face the audience and then swiftly bowed. He then turned round ninety degrees and looked at the orchestra spread out before him. Slowly he lifted his baton and looked directly at the first violins. He lowered the baton and the lead violin started the music. Swiftly the other violins and violas joined in to complete the string section. Then the percussion section came in, adding a 4/4 beat, giving the sound some extra energy.
Next the brass section joined in, with the horns and the trumpets giving power and volume to the music. Finally, the woodwind section with the clarinets and bassoons joined in and completed the group, so that a top edge could be heard. Now, the full orchestra was playing as one and the audience listening were focussed on what they could hear coming from the orchestra.
The conductor was starting to get into his role and his hair started to flop down over his brow. In an instant he pushed it back with his left hand whilst his right arm waved frantically. Many members of the audience began to lose themselves in the music as its spell wove different imaginings into their brains. Some tapped their fingers, others their feet. One or two even shook their heads in time to the music. It was as though everyone present was caught in a spell which took each individual far away from their everyday lives and into another world.

One of the great human achievements is that of music. It is one form of energy which is unique to the humans. It is based on vibrations which produce sounds, which are picked up by the human ear and are carried to the human brain to be processed. Originally humans only communicated through words and this was spoken by the humans. As time went on humans learnt that they could make other sounds with their tongues and their throats through their vocal chords and the idea of "singing" began. Most humans liked the sounds they were making and If the human chose to add words to the music, this became a "song". Gradually stories about human life began to be passed down from one generation to the next through song. Songs could make people calmer or happier, or it could have the effect of stirring people into aggression as in the period immediately before a battle.

Along with the sounds of music that came through the voices of humans, the sounds of music also came through "instruments" which humans created. These varied from simple stones hitting the ground to make the sound, or skins of animals used to make "drums", or strings on pieces of wood that have made "violins" and "guitars". This creativity led to the development of other instruments such as ones that involve blowing breath into a metal tube such as a "flute" or a "trumpet". The humans gradually realised that these instruments could make various sounds and eventually music, especially if they were played together they could make play the same notes from different instruments.

So, music could be in the form of songs with words coming out of the mouth in a musical way, or music could be without words and this was known as "instrumental" music, as you have just seen in the above event-capture. Whether the music is instrumental or vocal, music has sounds which have a range which can be high or low. The sounds have been called "notes" by the humans and can last for a short or a long time. For music to occur the human must first think of the sounds he or she wants to create. These notes or sounds are put together by a human creating the music and this piece of music is called a "composition". Usually, the music that is created will cause a human being listening to it to feel happy and contented as it has the effect of raising the vibrations inside the human body.

Gradually, music has evolved over the years from small groups of people playing instruments into larger groups called "orchestras", which perform "classical" music in an event called a "concert". This is where humans who have created their own music enjoy giving it to other human beings to hear. At first this was inside a building, but in more recent times humans have started to meet together in a place like a park or a field to hear this music being performed.

As time went on a human invention called "electricity" was invented and this meant that instruments could be powered by this energy form in instruments like "guitars" and "keyboards". It was much louder and started off being called "rock 'n' roll" and "pop" music and was liked by the younger humans. Now all sorts of music has developed through the creativity of humans with names like "reggae", "electronic", "house", "punk" and "folk" music. So, now in the present time there are myriads of types of music available and it is played all over the world and all the time, so that humans can listen to it whenever they want and wherever they are.

Clothes and fashion

Now, I will show you an aspect of human creativity that involves the whole body. It is known as wearing "clothes" or garments on the human body. This is unusual for us as we have no need for clothes, yet the humans have a need to wear clothes, not just for heat to protect them from the cold, but also as a way of expressing themselves as humans. Let me show you how this works.

Location – Milan, Italy – the catwalk of a fashion show

"Ladies and gentlemen", the announcer spoke. "I would like to begin the show with the latest portfolio from Michel De La Roux, an up-and-coming fashion designer from Paris".
Some loud, booming house music came out of the speakers high above the audience and the lights faded slightly. A tall female model appeared at the end of the catwalk, showing no expression on her face at all. She was wearing a sky-blue jacket made out of cotton, which covered a cream-coloured satin shirt. Her skirt matched the jacket and she wore cream-coloured high heels.

As she started to walk slowly along the catwalk the announcer began to describe her outfit, all the while the model looking straight ahead. She passed the audience who were seated at right angles to the catwalk. It was mainly buyers from several high street fashion shops, as well as fashion magazine editors and various members of the press. As soon as she reached the other end, she turned around and looked right ahead to where she had come from. She took off the jacket and hung it over her right shoulder and then started to walk back along the catwalk.

Some members of the audience took notes, whilst many more were filming the event on their mobile phones. As soon as she reached the end of the catwalk, a male model appeared, wearing a pea green velvet suit, with a black bowler hat on his head and a silver walking stick in his hand. He then proceeded to do everything the first model had done, all without any expression on his face.

Clothes are worn by all humans. They started off as basic skins from animals they had killed and they wore them to protect the human body from both the cold and hot temperatures in the places where they first lived. Then over the ages the types of clothing that the humans wore has changed with the ways in which the humans have developed. Clothes came to be made out of the natural materials that they learnt to harvest from the Earth.

Many humans, but especially the female of the species have become very mindful of the clothes that they wear. It is not enough to keep wearing the same clothes day by day and year by year. Instead, they have a strong need to keep changing the clothes they wear from one day to the next. So, something that they wear one day, will be left in their clothes space never to be worn again, or perhaps once more, before they feel that it is no longer "in fashion". "Fashion" by the way is the word that the humans have created to describe this idea of what is necessary to wear to be accepted by other humans.

In fact, so popular and influential is this idea, that a whole industry exists to promote the wearing and changing of particular clothes on particular days and in particular seasons. They have special places called "shops" where the humans can try on and wear these clothing items, before exchanging their money to buy them. Millions of humans love to go shopping as they call it, or more recently to partake of "retail therapy". Yes, you might be amazed to learn that some of the humans actually take great pleasure in choosing and trying on the different clothes.

Some humans have tried to combat this individuality in the humans by making all the humans in a certain group all wear the same sort of clothes. This is known as wearing a "uniform" and indicates to other humans what particular group these humans belong to, or what job the human does.

Humans have not only created clothes to cover their body which they wear, but also pieces of metal, glass, and plastic which they wear on their bodies. They call these pieces "jewellery". Now jewellery can take all forms and shapes. For instance, the humans might melt and mould metal ores from the earth and change them into things called necklaces which they wear round their necks, or bracelets which they wear around their wrists. They do this as a form of decoration to make their bodies look more attractive to other human beings, and also as a way of saying that they have status. That is the idea that they are more important than other human beings.

The way they do this is by the type of metal that they wear on their bodies. You see the humans place special significance on the type of metal they make this jewellery from. So, the metals of silver, gold and platinum are seen as showing prestige, power and affluence by the humans. Whilst other metals like copper, tin and brass are seen as being less valuable in human terms and so are worn by poorer humans.

The other type of jewellery worn by humans that they see as important is a small piece of metal which goes around their fingers of their hands and is called a "ring". This has a stronger value and influence than other sorts of jewellery. A ring around a particular finger means that you are connected strongly with another human being in the important relationship, usually called "marriage" which I have already mentioned earlier in my report. So, it means you are tied or committed to this other person by the fact that you wear this ring around your first finger on the left hand side.

Sometimes a human wearing a ring on another finger may also indicate that you are an important human by the fact that you wear a particular ring. You could be a king, queen or leader of your country and you wear that ring to show that you are important and above all other humans in a particular region of the Earth. Apart from metal, humans also use the coloured stones that are found inside the Earth for decorating their pieces of jewellery. These stones have the name of emerald, topaz, ruby and diamond according to their colour. Humans love these coloured stones in their jewellery and take great pleasure in wearing these.

Next I will tell you about a type of creative moving that the humans have invented which they call "sports". It is a general term which refers to lots of different activities that the humans practise which are also known as "games". Let me show you.

Sport and Competition

Location – Brussels, Belgium: a sports stadium

The crowd of eighty thousand spectators were cheering the female athletes on as they moved out of their lanes and into formation on the second lap of the women's 1500 metres final. For the athletes it was the culmination of years of hard work and sacrifice to get to this stage in their careers. It was crucial that they kept their focus, as the prize of a gold medal beckoned, as well going down in history as the best athlete in your discipline. The crowd's attention momentarily moved from the track to the field as a Hungarian male athlete launched a javelin across the green turf of the field part of the stadium. A huge cheer went up as his javelin passed the seventy metre mark. A few seconds later the monitors confirmed the distance thrown and that it was the longest throw so far that day.
The majority of the spectators moved their attention back to the track where the ringing of the bell indicated that there was just one lap to go. The tension in the crowd increased as the female athletes stepped up a gear and the field began to split

up into the weaker and the stronger. With just fifty metres to go the American pulled away from the Finn and managed to cross the line a whole two seconds ahead of her nearest rival. Meanwhile many people in the crowd had noticed an athlete hobbling along the track towards the finish line. They all stood on their feet, cheering and clapping her, urging her on to finish the race. Slowly, she made it to the end, collapsing onto the pink running track, well behind the rest of the other athletes.

In this event-capture you can see some humans running around a running track in a sport known as "athletics". This is just one of many different activities which the humans have invented where they move about and try to be "better" than other human beings who are also taking part in this sport. From an early age the humans have always played "games" where they will try and do something which involves beating another human being in the game. The best human is known as the "winner", whilst the rest of the humans are known as the "losers". Over time the humans have created all sorts of games to play with each other many of which use a sphere known as a "ball".

Many humans have this obsession of playing various games with a ball. They throw, catch, hit, kick, punch and carry this ball around a piece of ground, watched by many more humans on the edge. These games have got so organised that various rules have developed as to how a particular game must be played. It is always between two groups of humans, or just two humans. In the past the games were mainly played by males, but in recent times more and more females are now playing these games. Their games have different names like "football", "rugby", "cricket", "hockey" and "basketball", according to their "rules", which are the way these games have to be played. These games or sports are watched by hundreds and in many case thousands of other humans in specially built buildings called arenas and stadiums. Then millions more watch these games in their boxes in their homes.

It is difficult to explain to a non-human like yourself as to why these games are so popular amongst humans, but if you go down to Earth and observe a game you will notice the following. The humans will all be shouting at the same time and in some cases arguing with each other, and in extreme cases fighting with each other. Then if one of the players on the ground places the sphere in a certain part of the field or pitch, the whole crowd explodes in joyous celebrations, as if this is the most important thing on Earth!

There are some sports that involve just two humans opposing each other trying to win the game they are playing. Sometimes this involves hitting a sphere across a net as in the game called "tennis", or hitting a sphere into a hole, as in "golf". Sometimes it actually involves the two humans hitting each other! This may be with their hands or feet, or "weapons" which are pieces of metal which not only hurts the human being hit but can also damage the human's body. In some cases, so much so that they stop living on Earth.

I must now show you something which is the opposite of all the above, which can be said to be positive things. In fact, the humans can also be negative in what they create. Here is an example of one of the most negative things some humans are creating.

Armaments

Location – Lahore, Pakistan: the production line of an armaments factory

The hooter blew bang on time at 8.00 am to signal the start of the day shift at the armaments factory. The production line started flowing and all the various workers got into position, ready to do the same task for the next eight hours, with three breaks in between. Some of them had the job of placing the empty shell cases onto the production line conveyor belt,, whilst others lifted the completed shells onto specially built reinforced trestles. After about two hours of non-stop work the conveyor belt started to slow down. One of the workers sitting next to the conveyor belt knew what was coming. With a shudder it came to a halt. "Where's Ali?" he shouted. Another of the workers knew the drill and got up from his seat, walked quickly to the stairs and went up to where Ali's office was. He knocked urgently at the door.

Ali had been employed at the factory for almost seven years and he liked his job. He had a regular shift from eight in the morning until four in the afternoon, which meant that he was able to see his two children every day when they came home from school. He was the floor manager and had quite a bit of responsibility with twenty workers on the production line beneath him. What he hated most was when the production line came to a halt, as it meant potentially a loss of earnings if it wasn't sorted out quickly.

As soon as he heard the knock on his door he knew what had happened. Instantly he was on his feet and swung open the door. "Don't tell me. The belts got stuck again!" he said to the worker before he had a chance to open his mouth. He rushed down the stairs, past the boxes full of shells and bullets ready to go to dispatch. He came to the conveyor belt and bent down. He looked all along it both ways and then got up. He walked further down it and bent down again. He spotted what the problem was and pulled out a small screw which had come loose from a rogue shell further down the conveyor belt. He held it up in triumph and pressed the start button. Everything swung into action again. He could get back to his cup of coffee and more and more shells and bullets could be produced by the factory once more.

In the above event-capture you will probably have been amazed at what these humans are doing. Yes they are actually creating objects called "weapons" which will be used to hurt other humans and even stop them from existing on Earth. The weapons they are making are called "bullets" and "shells" and are similar in design, with the bullets being quite small in size and the shells being much bigger. They both have an ingredient inside them which will cause a large amount of energy to come out of them so that any human who is near these weapons when they land will certainly be hurt very badly or even killed.

"Why do the humans create such things?" you may ask. The simple answer is a human attitude or emotion called, "fear". This is when humans are afraid of each other and think that other humans will try and attack them and hurt them. So, in order to stop the other humans from doing hurtful things towards them they create these objects which are collectively known as "weapons" or "armaments", or "arms" for short. The problem is that the other humans that they are afraid of will be thinking and doing exactly the same thing! So, they too create these weapons. They also create much stronger weapons called "bombs". These can not only kill individual human beings but also kill very large numbers of humans in their thousands and millions. This process of fighting with weapons is known as "war" and I will tell you more about it later on in my report.

In this final section of this part of my report, I want to tell you about another aspect of human creativity called "Science". It can be used for either positive or negative outcomes for the humans.

Science

Location – Ingelheim, Germany: the laboratory of a drugs company

Peter had just returned to the lab from his coffee break. He picked up his white coat from its hanger in the corner and walked over to his work desk, putting on his coat on the way. He sat down and took a pair of disposable white gloves from out of the drawer, before putting them on. He then proceeded to pick up a culture in a glass container and held it up to the light. "Not much change there, he thought. Maybe I'd better double check this through the microscope. So, he put the container under the lens and carefully lowered the lens so it was just above the culture. He then adjusted the focus and looked down. He could see reddish purple cells surrounded by even more creamy yellow cells. "Yes!" he spoke out loud. "Come and look at this, Angela! I think we've made a breakthrough here." Angela hurried over from her chair, took off her glasses and looked down the microscope. "Oh my God!" she exclaimed. The cancer cells are dying. That experiment you did is working. Well done Peter! Maybe we have made the first steps in finding a cure for this type of cancer?"

Science is a human activity which is done by the humans known as "scientists" who are always researching and analysing different things on the planet. They want to find out how everything on the planet works and what can be done to improve the lives of humans on Earth. Science can also be used in a negative way when the scientists use it to develop new weapons that can be used to hurt or kill other humans as in the previous event-capture. Though most of the time the scientists are more interested in making new discoveries that will be of help to other humans as in this event-capture.

Scientists are very creative in what they do, though it is a different type of creative than most of the examples above. Sometimes though they can be quite stubborn when they think they have all the answers to the questions they are asking and will not accept new ideas from other humans as it doesn't fit in with what they say. This can sometimes lead to arguments and worse between the scientists and the other humans when they can't agree on something. Overall though the work that scientists do is of benefit to the other humans.

Part 8

Human Feelings

Just one more year and then you'll be happy

Freedom of choice

Human beings are motivated by their feelings. It is difficult to explain what a feeling is as we do not experience this on our planet apart from the continuous state of being of love. The human beings have all sorts of feelings, some of them positive to them, and some of them negative to them. I will look at several of them below in this section of my report, but first I must tell you about the basic system which is behind all human feelings and that is freedom of choice.

This concept which they call "choice" enables their decisions to proceed in different directions rather than one way which is what we do on our planet. I know that must be very hard for you to understand as on our planet we are all of one mind and one purpose. But it means that the humans are able to have different ways to go in their thinking and creating processes, as opposed to one single action which we have. It makes life on Earth for the human beings very interesting; or difficult in some cases, because at various times they cannot agree on the best way forward.

They have another concept closely associated with choice where they say something is either "right" or "wrong", a type of duality and it is this which causes the most amount of disagreements amongst the humans. One group of humans will say they are right and a different group will say they are wrong, whilst the second group we say, "No! We are right and you are wrong!" Of course, we know that there is no such thing as right and wrong. It is merely a case of one group thinking one thing and another group thinking a different thing.

The problems start for the humans when a large group of human beings have the belief that they are "right", whilst a smaller group of human beings are told that they are "wrong". As they are wrong they must change their belief system to what the majority believe, otherwise the large group will start doing various things to the small group to make them change their beliefs. This notion has been with most human beings ever since the Change happened and it has led to many different confrontations between human beings ever since. You will see some examples of this below.

Fear

The human emotion known as "fear" is the one negative feeling that dominates human thought and behaviour more than anything else in human beings. It is something that many humans are not able to deal with. They give in to it and let this emotion take over their lives so that they are literally "living in fear". Let me show you an example of this in action.

Location – Sao Paulo, Brazil: the bedroom of a flat

"Mummy! Mummy! shouted the little girl in terror as she woke up from the nightmare she had just had. Her mother had heard her screaming and instantly woke up. She rushed into her daughter's bedroom and lifted her up into her arms, cradling her head in her hands.

"It's alright darling. Mummy's here. Don't worry. I'm here now".

"Mummy. There was a monster chasing me", she stuttered out the words, still in fear. "He nearly got me!"

Her mother held her closer to her and stroked the back of her head.

"I'll protect you, dear. I won't let any monster get you. You're safe with me and daddy".

"But I'm afraid he'll get me when I get back into my bed", she stated.

"No, he won't!" said the mother, trying to reassure her daughter.
"But he will!" pleaded the little girl. "I just know he will!"
There was nothing that the mother could do or say that would placate the girl's fear. There was only one thing left for the mother to say.
"OK Darling. If you promise that you will stop crying and that this is only time we will do this, mummy will let you sleep in her bed?"
The little girl immediately stopped her crying and looked up into her mother's eyes.
"I promise mummy".

The little human you have just seen in this event-capture is in an extreme state of fear, which some humans call being "terrified". This is when the feeling of fear takes over a human being so much that they aren't able to function normally and just need someone to protect and comfort them. This of course is the most extreme type of fear that humans have, but fear can exhibit itself in human behaviour in lots of different ways, some of which I will discuss below.

Most of the time when humans show fear they are "afraid" that something negative will happen to them. It might be that they might not pass their exam, or that someone will physically hurt them, or that they will get punished for something they haven't done, and so on.

Some humans have learnt that if other humans are afraid they can exploit them and get them to do something that they might not normally do. For example, they might be able to get them to hand over their possessions or money because they are afraid that the other human will hurt them. Or they will obey what the other human wants them to do, even though they don't want to do it because they are afraid of the other human. I will go into this in more detail in another part of my report. Finally, when humans are in a state of fear they also exhibit another type of human feeling, which is closely connected to fear and that is the notion of "worry". Let me show you this in action.

Worry

In the first event-capture of this section of my report you will have seen the notion of choice in action. It also shows you a smaller part of the choice action in that the human is choosing to think that the worst thing is going to happen in the future. This is known as "worry". Here many human beings have the notion that something negative is going to happen to them or other humans close to them. They think that this negative action will happen even though when the event does happen it is usually a positive thing. Let me show you an example of this in action.

Location – Freiburg, Germany: the bedroom of a suburban detached house

Monica and her husband, Kurt, were about to go out for the evening to a performance of Wagner's opera, Siegfried at the local theatre. They would be guests of the mayor and his council so Monica was concerned that she should show herself and her husband in a good light.
"Which dress do you think I should wear, darling? The red one, or the green one?" she asked.
"Oh, I think the green one would be more suitable?" he replied.
She quickly put the green dress on and then sat at the dressing table. She picked two pairs of silver earrings from out of her jewellery box and held them up. The first pair contained a row of five diamonds, which glistened in the light; whilst the second pair, contained just one large diamond encrusted in an oval silver frame.
"Which set of earrings should I wear, Kurt? she enquired once more.
"I think the long, dangly pair would be better with the green dress", he replied decisively.
Monica followed Kurt's advice and put on the second pair. When she looked in the mirror she had her doubts.
"Are you sure they look OK, Kurt?" she asked her husband with a worried expression on her face.

"Yes!" he replied showing a hint of exasperation in his reply.
"Just stop worrying. Everything will be fine!"
Next, Monica pulled out three pairs of shoes from her
wardrobe and tried each pair on in turn. She just couldn't
make up her mind as to which pair to wear.
"Oh, I'm really not sure which pair of shoes to wear tonight,
darling. What do you think?"
"The second pair", called Kurt from across the bedroom, not
even looking at the shoes. "If we don't hurry up, we shall miss
the start!"
But Monica would not be rushed. She was so worried about
not looking perfect before all those local dignitaries.
"Do you think the children will be alright with Moira?" she
asked, showing concern in her voice. "I know she has babysat
before, but what if the children won't go to bed when she
says? What if they won't settle?"
"They'll be perfectly OK!" replied Kurt sounding more than
firm in his reply. "We are going out for a special evening and
we will enjoy it. So please stop worrying!"

I mentioned earlier in my report the concept of pain which affects the human body. Humans also put into practise another version of pain in the way they think. This is pain of their mind which they call "worry". This is when a human being focuses on some aspect of their human lives that they cannot control or alter and they keep focusing on this thing, again and again, until they create a type of mental pain within themselves. It could be about a human relationship that is not functioning as it should be, or whether something hasn't happened in a way that they hoped would happen. The humans call such things as these, "problems". The strange thing is that these events haven't happened yet in human time, yet they think they will happen, even if they don't!
The only way that they can deal with this mental pain is to deal with the problem that is causing them to worry. This is how the human body works in dealing with a physical pain. Yet humans don't always deal with their mental pains as quickly as they could do. Sometimes all they have to do is talk through the problem with another human and perhaps see it from a different point of view. Sometimes the human needs to

be mentally strong and deal with the problem themselves, rather than doing nothing about it. All problems on Earth could easily become "solutions" if only the humans would learn to talk things through with each other and stop worrying about the worst possible outcome of something that is worrying them.

Vanity

Another feeling that humans have which in many ways is connected with the concept of worry is that of "vanity". This is the human idea that their bodies and especially their faces have to look a certain way, otherwise other humans won't like them or love them. Sometimes this fear of not being liked by other humans makes them do things to their bodies and faces which permanently changes them. Here is one such example in action.

Location – Ankara, Turkey - the surgery of a dentist

The young lady was nervously sitting in the waiting room for her operation to begin. She had flown out from the UK to Turkey on the promise of better looking teeth. She had spent all of her savings as well as taking out a huge loan to pay for the operation. The surgeon would change her jagged teeth into a lovely white perfect smile. That's what the advert had said. She kept getting her mirror out and smiling and imagining what a new smile would look like once the operation was completed. She had heard about the risks but decided that the outcome would be worth it in the end. She could take lots of painkillers to dumb to pain. A door opened from the surgeon's office and a man appeared dressed in surgical clothing with a mask over his mouth.
"Good morning Miss Jamieson!" he said with a broken English accent. "I'm glad that you have decided to use us to transform that smile of yours. If you could just sign this form which explains everything and then we can get started".
Miss Jamieson didn't bother looking at the various terms and conditions which explained that the surgeon and his company

wouldn't be liable if anything went wrong. Instead, she quickly
scribbled her signature and handed the form back to the man.
"If you will follow me, we can get started"...........

It is time now to look at a problem which many human beings
seem to have about the way they look. We all look the same
and are quite content with how we look, but human beings are
different. They give the two extremes of how they look the
names of "beauty" and "ugliness". This is where human
beings have this inherent weakness that makes them think they
are not good enough to be the human that they are. They have
this idea that all other humans are better than they are - better
looking, have a better body shape, are not as large as they are,
are stronger than they are, have more money than they have,
have a nicer girlfriend/boyfriend, husband, wife than theirs,
and so on.

This leads to humans going to all sorts of lengths to change
their looks or their body weight. They do this by putting
different chemicals onto their faces known as "make-up" or by
putting different substances into their body to make them lose
weight, or to put weight on, or to change their skin colour.
They even go so far as to have operations to change or remove
parts of their body. Even though this might cost them a lot of
money and make them have a huge debt of money to someone
else, they deem this necessary to achieve the look that they
think will make them feel better about themselves. This isn't
helped by all sorts of magazines and newspapers and the
adverts in them that promote the idea that you should not be
content with the way you look naturally.

Jealousy

Another feeling that humans have which comes from the main
concept of worry is a feeling called "jealousy" when they feel
that they own another human being, not realising that each
human being is in charge of their own life. They feel that this
other human being is their own possession and if they do
something that the human who thinks they owns then doesn't
like, that human will get angry with them and may even hurt

them either by their words or by their actions. This feeling of jealousy is something that takes over the minds of so many humans that they don't think of the consequences of their actions. Let me show you an example of this.

Location - Karachi, Pakistan: a man accusing his wife of an alleged affair *

The man looked angrily at his wife of two years. "You've been cheating on me, you bastard!". His wife looked terrified and bowed her head.

"I swear to God that I haven't!" she replied quietly. "Why would I be unfaithful to the man I love?"

"That's not true", her husband shouted in reply. "I know you've been seeing another man behind my back!"

"It's just hearsay from your enemies who want to shame you and me", she countered, but her husband wouldn't believe her.

"You're a lying bitch!" he screamed at her. "I know you're lying to me. Your very own brother, Ahmed told me".

"No! He's just making it up as he's jealous of me as we are so much richer than he is!"

"Enough! I will not listen to your lies a minute longer!

With that he pulled the cork out of the glass bottle he was holding and threw the contents straight at her face. It was acid and his wife immediately screamed out in agony, falling to the floor in extreme pain. Her skin was burning with an intense heat, the like of which she had never before experienced. Her husband, ignoring her screams, looked down on her coldly.

"Let that be a lesson to you. Never mess with me again. A transgression like that deserves a strong punishment. You must learn never to cross me. You're no longer my wife!"

The activity you have just seen is one that many humans exhibit. This is when one human being sees another human being as their own possession and not an individual in their own right. Or they want something that another person has yet they aren't able to have this thing, perhaps because they do not have the money to buy this thing, or the other human being carries attributes that the other wants. They then develop the feeling of being jealous of the other human being. They want this thing so much that they do hurtful things to the other human being to get it.

Or sometimes if they think that the other human has behaved in a way that they do not like they become jealous with rage and decide that they must "get even with" the human who has hurt or angered them. This is called "revenge" and in a way once they have done something unpleasant to the person they seem not jealous anymore. Yet on the other hand the person who has been hurt will be emotionally hurt inside, which will stay with them for a very long time.

Closely connected with this feeling is one called "anger" and here it is in action.

Anger

Location – Cork, Ireland: a traffic warden about to put a ticket on a car

Stuart Black had waited until his favourite quiz programme had finished in spite of his wife nagging him to hurry up and collect the prescription before the doctor's surgery shut. He had then driven the two miles to the doctor's surgery, making sure that he got there before it shut for the night. If he was quick he could drop off the prescription at the nearby chemists and get it sorted before that too shut for the night. Otherwise, he would have to come back tomorrow and pick up the medicine after work had finished for the day.

However, when he got to the doctors the car park was full, so he decided to take a chance and park on the double yellow lines on the main road. After all it was after 5 o'clock and the traffic wardens would have finished for the day. He parked his car, locked the door, and rushed across the road and into the surgery.

Unfortunately, there was a queue so he had to wait a few minutes until it was his turn. He swiftly picked up the green

sheet of paper from the receptionist and turned and walked out of the surgery only to find a man standing by his car. As he got closer he could see the man was holding a notepad and pen and was in fact a ticket warden writing out a parking ticket.

"Hold on there!", Stuart shouted, "I've only been gone less than a minute". The traffic warden looked up momentarily, but ignored Stuart, continuing to write on his notepad.

"Excuse me!" shouted Stuart who was getting more angry by the minute. "You're not giving me a ticket are you?" The warden then tore a the top sheet off from his pad. It was coloured yellow and black. He lifted a windscreen wiper and placed the ticket under it and started to walk away.

"Do you mind?!" shouted Stuart who was getting exasperated. "That's my property you're fiddling with!"

The traffic warden replied, "And that's the council's road that you're illegally parked on!"

"Oh, come on! It's not as though I've been parked there all day. Two bloody minutes that's all" he pleaded.

The warden simply said, "If you pay the fine within two weeks, it's only forty Euros. Otherwise, it's double that!" And with that he walked away. Stuart wanted to hit the traffic warden hard in his face but realised that would only make things worse. He lifted the windscreen wiper and picked up the yellow and black ticket, still fuming....

You have just seen an example of anger in action, where one human being wants or expects something to happen in a certain way, yet when it doesn't they show the feeling of anger. Basically, they are not getting their "own way" and so react in this way. The very young humans known as babies and children often show this emotion as they are constantly learning about the best way to behave being taught by their parents or teachers. Yet some many adult human beings exhibit this behaviour in just the same way as the young humans do as they haven't matured enough to stop their anger from happening. Some humans would not react with anger in a situation like this but would accept the ticket and "move on" as the humans say. "It has happened – So what!"

Sometimes the anger in human beings gets so great that it consumes them with a feeling called "hatred". Let me show you this.

Hatred

Location – North Korea: prison camp Number 44 *

Prisoner 34256 crawled on all fours towards the prison guard who was dishing out a soup like concoction, with a rusty ladle. The prisoner's bony hands held on tightly to his metal bowl, which was dented and blackened with age, but this was the only thing that kept him alive in this hell hole. His body was totally emaciated from a mixture of over-work and starvation. The little flesh there was on his body, clung onto the bony framework, which could hardly be called a body. Yet the guard on the other hand was bulky and overweight, with not one iota of humanity left in his bitter looking eyes.

The prisoner nervously held up his bowl to the guard, who spat in it, laughed and poured what looked like half measures of the "soup" into it. Prisoner 34256, overcome with hunger pangs, snatched the bowl from the guard and furiously gulped down the awful tasting mixture. Thwack! A blow from the guard onto his left cheek knocked him sideways and the remaining contents of the bowl deposited themselves onto the dusty floor on the prison hut.

"You fucking shite!" shouted the guard, as the prisoner recovered enough to start licking up any traces of liquid from the bowl. Now, move!"

Another blow came from the guard – this time with his right foot – and landed into the prisoner's rib cage and sent him several feet across the room.

"Get out of here you bastard!" snarled the guard, who easily lifted up the lightweight prisoner and flung him into the far corner of the hut.

"Oh dear! You just used up the rest of your dinner!" he said with a sneer in his voice. The prisoner fainted at that point, giving him a brief respite from the bullying guard.

One of the things I must tell you is that some human beings

don't care for other human beings. I know that is difficult to understand, but they don't just not like other human beings, they actually "hate" them. This is when a human feels intense dislike of someone, so much so that they could actually hurt them badly or worse. Now of course you know that hate comes from fear. Much of this hatred is borne out of a fear that another human being looks different to them, or they don't hold the same views as them, or they don't dress in the same way as them. Many of these human beings can't cope with the fact that other human beings have different coloured skin to them and so they persecute them because of this.

Other groups of humans don't like those who speak in a different language to them or have a different accent to them. Or they hate humans that are a different size or shape to them. This is known as "bullying" and this is where those humans who were really afraid of the other humans might say horrible words to them to hurt them in their minds. Sometimes they even hit them with their hands or kick them with their feet as they were so afraid of them as in the event-capture. I know that on our planet we do not do these actions because we all love each other, but on Earth some humans do these things. However, there are some enlightened humans who say this is not the way to live and they try to stop this happening. But most human being are not bothered about this bullying and just continue on with their daily lives, choosing to ignore that this is going on.

Lust

One aspect of feelings that humans have for each other is one where they want to have something so strongly that another human has, they are prepared to hurt the other human in doing so. They desire to "get" or "have" that human so much that they will do anything to achieve this desire. This desire is especially strong in the male human and can cause so much hurt and distress to the other human that they desire. When they desire this human so much in a sexual way it is called "lust" by the humans. Most of the time it is the human males showing the behaviour of lust towards human females, though sometimes it could be to other human males as well. In some cases, it might be the other way round with the human female having the feeling of lust towards the human male or again on occasion to another human female.

However, there are some male humans who do not have any respect for the female humans and they think they can do what they like to the female humans. Here is one example.

Location – Belfast, Northern Ireland: a woman making her way home *

It had been a great night out for Laura. She had been clubbing until the early hours and had drunk way too much alcohol. Her mates had all gone home leaving her by herself in the club. She wasn't bothered about finding a man to go home with. In fact, she was going through a stage when she felt that she was better off being single. "Men are just trouble!" was her attitude. It was more fun hanging around with her female friends, but they had gradually drifted away as the night wore on. Now it was time for chucking out and although she was tipsy, she knew which way the taxi rank was. In just twenty minutes she could be home and in bed, sleeping like a baby.
Yet when she got to the taxi rank there was such a long queue that she couldn't be bothered to wait. "I may as well walk home. It'll be quicker than hanging around for a cab to arrive". So, buoyed up by Dutch courage from her alcohol and not thinking of her own safety, she started walking the two miles home. Her head was spinning and she thought back to the wonderful night that she had just had. After a mile she sat down on the pavement to catch her breath. The night was warm.
Little did she know that a lone male also walking home after a night out had been following her. At first he hadn't paid much attention to her, but then the thought that he could easily have her had entered his mind. Laura looked at her watch and it said 3.35 am. She got up and began walking again. She had a sudden feeling that she was being watched and turned around. As she looked a hand came over her mouth and an arm crushed her arms together. She tried to scream, but no sound

would come out of her mouth. Her assailant forced her into an alley way and turned her face to the wall, pinning her so there was no escape. With his other hand he started to grab at her clothes..........

This event-capture shows the worst aspect of lust as shown by a human male against a human female. He does not care about her feelings or show respect to her own private space. All he wants to do is to connect with her sexually. If she does not want to do this, he is not going to stop. When a human male does this to a human female it is called "rape". It causes so much stress in the human female that she gets the feelings of hurt inside her and changes her behaviour to such an extent that she almost becomes a different human. She may well not want to go out socially anymore. She may be afraid of being alone outside and she will certainly not trust human males from now on. The human male on the other hand who has done this act, will not be concerned about the feelings of the female he has attacked. He may even see it as a conquest and because he has done it once, may well try to do it again as it feeds some sort of need inside him.

There are of course human laws that say the male human should be punished for doing this, but first he must be caught and justice served on him. This can be quite a difficult thing to do as the female human might be afraid to take the matter further. Or other humans might not believe her and say that she is telling lies. In some human countries it happens so often, that the humans there accept it as something that is part of everyday life and don't bother to seek justice. Sometimes the relatives of the female human decide to punish the male human who did this rape and attack or even kill this human as "revenge". Most humans do see events like this as something wrong that must be righted.

Loneliness

Another feeling that many humans have is that of "loneliness". This is when a human feels that they are apart from other humans. They feel isolated from other human beings and think that no one is concerned about them. Let me show you this from a human point of view.

Location – Glasgow, Scotland: on the seventeenth floor of a block of flats

The old age pensioner looked out of her window to the scene far below her. There was white everywhere as a fresh fall of snow had fallen in the night. She was colder than she had ever been in all her life and seeing that snow made her shiver even more. She moved over to her electric fire to turn it on, but suddenly pulled away. She had made a vow that between the hours of nine and five she would not switch it on. This was because her last bill had meant that she had gone without food at lunchtimes for two weeks so she could afford to pay it.

She thought of putting on the television to take her mind off things, but again it would use up so much electricity and she knew she couldn't afford it. If only the government could see the state she was in. Her pension was simply not enough to pay for all these bills, let alone provide her with enough food to live on. Oh, how she wished that she was twenty years younger and could be working again. At least she'd have someone to talk to and she would have more than enough money for her needs. But now at the end of her days, she felt lonely and forgotten and wished that death would soon take her.

Her two children lived miles away and she hardly ever saw them as they did not like coming to the area where she lived. Plus, they would be at work at this time of day. Her next door neighbours were also out working and the club for the over-50s that she used to go to had been shut by the local council as they had run out of funding to pay for it. 'Other services must take priority', they said. She no longer had a phone as she just couldn't afford the bills, and she knew if she did have one, she would be scared to talk too long, in case she made the cost go up. Oh, how she missed her husband who had died three years earlier. If he were still here now she would be able to talk to someone and wouldn't feel so alone. It was so hard for her as the loneliness took over. No one cares anymore, she thought. If only I lived nearer my children she thought. She decided to go back to bed and sleep.

This event-capture shows what happens to some human beings, especially if they live by themselves with no one to talk to them. They become isolated as they are forgotten about by other human beings. In some cases when humans get older and they do not have any children they live by themselves. The friends they do have start to stop being humans and are no longer in their lives. So, they do not see other human beings for long periods of human time. As a result, they get "lonely". This is because humans are a social species who tend to live in groups, such as families or tribes, and so are used to having other human beings around them most of the time. They love to communicate with each other, usually by talking to each other, and when that stops happening for various reasons as the event-capture shows, they find it very hard and become lonely. The solution seems to be for other humans to organise different humans to make sure there are no lonely humans near where they live and to speak to each other more and help each other.

Coupled with loneliness is another feeling which is stronger than loneliness and stems from where a human stops being happy and contented. This can be for lots of reasons which I will tell you about below. But first let me show you this in an event-capture.

Depression

Location – Swansea, Wales: a mother in mourning for her son

Sophie Johnsoni was trying to keep busy by cleaning her house, so she wouldn't be thinking about Darren, her son, who was no longer alive. But as she was dusting in her living room she picked up a photo frame from the shelf in front of her and started to cry. The picture was of Darren, who had been killed on active duty in Iraq. He was only nineteen when he died, and although it was now many years since his death, to

Sophie it seemed like yesterday. She was still missing him terribly. She missed hearing his laughter as he watched his favourite sit com on the TV. She missed him coming in late at night after a night out with the lads and creeping up the stairs so as not to awaken her, even though she was still awake, worrying about when he was going to come home.

She missed him complimenting her on her cooking when she made him his favourite meal of roast beef and Yorkshire pudding. The tears rolled down her cheeks as she thought of these things. She still had two other children, who were both living nearby, but Darren was her baby and the loss she felt could not be healed. At first she went to his grave every day to put flowers there, but gradually this was now down to once a week. Even then she felt guilty at not doing it more often, but "Life goes on" as the saying said, she thought. "Will I ever get over this?" she questioned herself. She put the photo back on the shelf and continued with her dusting.

You can see here the idea here is of emotional attachment of one human being to another human being. This starts off from the moment a human being is born on Earth and is the bond of attachment between a mother and her baby. This bond continues growing right through the human's lifetime, until one of them leaves the Earth. Even then the one who is still on Earth will often think of the other human as though he or she were still present in their body on Earth.

They will miss this human very much and become sad whenever they think of this human as they are no longer there for them to communicate with them. It is a great loss when a human dies and those who are left behind keep thinking of them. The more they think about them, the more they miss them, and the more they miss them, the sadder they become. Gradually this sadness gets stronger within the human and they become very unhappy, or "depressed" as it is described by the humans.

This is one reason why someone becomes depressed - through losing the presence of another human being in their life. But humans can also become depressed for other reasons. One of them is losing their job where they work. It can make them very worried that they won't have enough money coming into their lives to pay for food and the bills they have to pay for. It can also make them sad as they do not have the human friends they had when they worked. It can also make them think that no one cares for them as they do not have a job like most humans do and so they are not as good as other humans.

Another thing that make humans depressed is that they do not have other human friends, especially a life partner, or a human child in their lives. Or that they do not have a human home to live in, or that they haven't got what another human has. They can then get more and more depressed until they get into a state which I shall show you now where they no longer want to exist as a human on the Earth.

Suicide

Location – Panama, Central America: a young man contemplating suicide

Roberto was hurting so much inside. The emotional pain he felt was unbearable and he couldn't see a way out. At just twenty-three he felt that his life was no longer worth living. It was now two weeks since his girlfriend of two years had broken off the relationship. They had been going steady for two years now, but she had given him the usual excuse of "wanting more freedom" and "not being tied down". Roberto on the other hand had seen it much differently. He had envisaged living the rest of his life with Justine, but he knew that wasn't going to happen now. At first he had pleaded with her to reconsider, but she wasn't having any of it and had now blocked him on her phone. "How can she just shut me out of her life? he thought.

He'd turned to his mother in his emotional anguish. She had replied with the maxim, "There's always plenty more fish in the sea", but that hadn't really helped either. He just wanted Justine. No one else could take her place. Now he was alone in his room feeling like shit. He was looking at Internet sites which had "Suicide" as the subject and there were plenty of them, in spite of the fact that there were laws banning these sort of sites. As he scrolled through the various websites he found several which gave him details of the different ways of taking your life. He was getting deeper and deeper into despair and it would only be a matter of time before he would follow suit.....unless someone could talk him out of this.

Here you can see the situation of where someone has decided that they don't want to live on Earth anymore. They have had enough of being a human on the planet and want to leave it. To do this they must deliberately stop themselves from living as a human, or "commit suicide" as it is called. When a human gets to this stage they are so depressed that they see doing this as the only thing they can do. So many humans end up doing this as they haven't been able to see any alternative to the situation they are in. For those who know them, especially their parents and partners and children, it is very sad and very hard for them to understand why they did this. Losing someone in this way affects them for the rest of their lives in some cases.

There are of course lots of reasons why the human should not commit suicide and some humans have organised themselves into groups which try and help humans who are feeling like this. In many cases they are successful in stopping a human from committing suicide, but there are always some humans who will still go ahead and stop their human lives whatever anyone else may do or say. What the humans need to do is help these depressed humans at a much earlier stage when they are starting to feel depressed. This does happen in some countries, but in others there is no one to help these humans and it still keeps happening.

You have now heard about a variety of feelings that human beings show, many of them quite negative. However, there is one feeling that all human beings are capable of feeling. In fact, all humans once had this feeling in abundance, and it is one that many do still exhibit. It is called "happiness" and here is an example of it.

Happiness

Location -- Christchurch, New Zealand: a couple walking in the woods

The middle aged man and the woman got out of the car and went towards the boot. The man lifted the boot door up and the excited dog, a Red Setter, jumped out of the back of the car, wagging its tail excitedly. It obediently let its master put its lead on him. It then followed the middle aged couple from the car park into the woods, all the while trying to sniff at whatever took his fancy. It was a pleasant spring day with several clumps of daffodils swaying in the gentle breeze.

Once they were away from the car park and into the woods, the man let the dog off its lead. It went bounding off ahead, stopping every so often to sniff at the bases of the trees. A group of Silvereyes flew nervously amongst the branches above. They would stop for a few seconds, before flying off again to land on another branch. If you listened, there were all sorts of birds singing in the background. Most of the trees were now starting to have buds on them and many birds were starting to build their nests in readiness for the next batch of their family.

It was one of those days when you were glad to be alive. The man held onto the hand of his wife and looked up, amazed at all the beauty around him. "The best things in life are free!" he said. They both looked into each other's eyes and kissed. They were blissfully happy.

Happiness is a state of human mind that only a small number of human beings are in during most of their time on Earth. It means that there are "contented" or "happy" and that none of the above negative emotions trouble their human minds. 'What makes humans happy?' you may ask. Well, there are lots of things that can make humans happy. Perhaps the biggest one is when they find another human being to share their life with, someone who becomes their partner. They may well be in the human mind state of "being in love" and wish to spend the rest of their time on earth with this other human.

Another important event which can make the humans feel happiness is when they become the parents of another human being. For the first time in their lives the humans realise that they are creators, not just of a material thing but of something that is living and is a part of them. They take joy in the human baby that they have created and will enjoy watching this baby grow first into a human child and then into a young human, and eventually into a human adult the same they are.

Of course, there are many other things that make a human happy such as achieving something they didn't think they were capable of such as academic success or having a home of their own to live in or having a pet to keep and look after. These are just some of the things that can make a human being have the state of happiness, but there are many other things that can make a human happy which you may have seen in other parts of my report.

As in this final event-capture above you can see the two human beings finding happiness in the simple event of just walking in the natural world away from all the pressures of everyday life. They see the beauty that is all around them and are thankful for it. That is what many humans miss experiencing as they are so caught up in the human activity of making money or travelling about the planet or worrying about some possible human event in the future which will probably not even happen.

So, you see that happiness is something that is obtainable for all human beings if they seek it and make time to relax and be away from all the pressures of everyday human life. If only all humans learnt to be grateful for the things they do have, rather than be unhappy for the things they do not have. Many humans are too busy allowing these other human feelings take over their lives which are negative in nature. They need to look for the positive feelings and then they would be much happier.

Part 9

Human Money

Money, so they say, is the root of all evil today

Consumerism

Before I start to tell you about one of the most important things to humans, I must briefly mention the need that humans have to possess different physical objects. They all seem to have an in-built system inside them which says that they must acquire different objects or "possessions" as they call them. This activity is known as "consumerism" and the humans who do this activity are called "consumers".
I know that in their earliest days that humans needed to collect natural things growing out of the Earth like nuts and berries, which they ate for food energy. But in more recent times many of the humans have started to accumulate more and more of the objects called possessions. These possessions are mainly things that have been created by the humans themselves They can be such things as clothes, jewellery, ornaments, antiques, toys, books, records, postage stamps, metal objects, pottery objects, pictures, paintings, furniture or vehicles.

Now it seems that in order to collect all these possessions the humans need give something in exchange for the possessions and this is where the concept of "money" comes in. Let me show you how money works for the humans.

Money

Location – Southend-on-Sea, England: the inside of a bank

"Good morning sir!", said the bank clerk. She was dressed in a bright red suit and wore a badge on her chest which displayed her name and position within the bank. "Is there anything that I can help you with?" she asked the man who had come in to deposit the cash takings from the previous evening. He owned a restaurant in the city and in spite of the number of people who paid with a debit card or credit card, he still had a fair few of his customers who preferred to pay with real money, or cash. Some of this cash was intended as tips for his staff, but he had a rule that all tips would be paid monthly in the staff wages, equally divided up so that it was fair for everyone.

He made his way through the bank towards the kiosks where two members of staff were busy dealing with customers. "This is going to take some time", he thought to himself. So, he got out his mobile phone and started looking through one of the many social media apps that were on his phone.

"Next please!" said the male clerk slightly to his right, just moments later. He hadn't noticed that the queue had quickly gone down and it was now his turn to be served. He moved forward and put the heavy bag of cash on the desk in front of him. The clerk lifted up his window and took the cash. He emptied its contents and coins in clear plastic bags fell out, along with some bundles of bank notes of different denominations, as well as two paying in books.

The clerk just got on with his job and started to sort the money out, making a note of each amount. When he had finished doing this, he opened the two paying in books and started ticking each different set of coins and notes until he was satisfied that everything was correct and in order.

The restaurant owner thought, "Maybe I could just go cashless in future? It would make life so much easier for me. But then that might mean this bank closing down as not enough people are using it. Oh. I don't know!"
"All correct!" said the clerk as he stamped the two paying in books and handed them back to the man.
Another visit to the bank was over.

In this event-capture you can see the human construct of "money" in action. All those coins and bank notes are called "cash" and they represent a transaction that one human being has made with another human being. In this case the transaction is "payment" by his customers for the food they have eaten in the restaurant. The owner of the restaurant will then gather up all the money that he has received and then take it to a bank or building society where it will be kept safely and securely in the owner's "account". If he wants any of the cash for other uses he can come back in to the bank and ask for it.

This is what humans do the world over with money. They "buy" something with money from someone who "sells" it to them. It might be for an object which the human wants to possess very much. Or it might be for a "service" such as providing food in this case, or giving advice to someone, or it might be for information of some kind such as in a book or on a computer. Everywhere I go on Planet Earth there is money to be seen. It is not all the same money though. Each country has its own set of money which is called "currency" which can only be used in that country, or in some cases in a group of countries. Names for these different currencies include Pounds, Dollars, Rouble, Yen, Rupee and so on.

However, not all money is cash. More and more money is being used as simple numbers on a computer screen. In theory the owner of that money should be able to go into any bank or building society and take that money out of their account in the form of cash, but in reality with the invention of the Internet people are using their money in a cashless form as numbers. They still buy and sell as they have done for thousands of years, but just use the numbers on their screens or on special pieces of plastic called "credit cards" or "debit cards". Let me show you and example of this.

Trade

Location – The City of London, England: the trading room of a major international bank

Simon McGregor was working hard, looking intently at the computer screen in front of him. Some lights were coloured green, but most of them were coloured red, which meant that the shares he was in charge of were falling in value. He spoke down his mouthpiece to Hong Kong. "Do you want to buy some stocks in Mercer's? Only one-fifty sterling each?" The voice at the other end said, "No. They're not worth the seat I'm sitting on!" and the phone line went dead.

He had been in this situation many times before and believed that his portfolio would rally by the end of the day. It would be OK. He was sure about that. He tried ringing Tokyo. Again, the response was just the same. So, he tried throwing in a different company's shares. "What about Goldberg's?" The voice at the other end of the line spoke in broken English, "I'm not too sure with your offer. If you could come down ten, I might be tempted."

"OK", replied Simon. "I'll meet you down ten". The light showing red for Goldberg's instantly changed to green on his monitor and he breathed a sigh of relief.

Things were starting to turn at last, he thought.

So here is an example of another human invention which is based on the exchange of money called "trade". This is basically exchanging money for an item or "commodity". This commodity could be a physical thing like metal or plastic, but it could also be a non-physical item like stocks and shares which are there on the screen and bought or sold for money. They can go up or down in "value" depending on how many people want to buy them or sell them. The person you see here is selling the commodity of shares which is his work. If he sells the shares for more than he paid them, he will make a "profit", but if he sells them for less than he paid for them he will make a "loss".

This is how he and many human beings "make a living", which is another phrase for accumulating enough money in their lives so that they can pay for all the things that they need to thrive on Planet Earth. This includes things like paying money for food, shelter, clothing, power sources and entertainment.

This basically is how virtually every human being spends most of their time on Earth so that they can survive. Some humans might make a lot of money in the work they do and so they have more money than they need to survive. These are known as "rich" humans, whilst those who hardly make any money and who do not have enough to pay for all those things are known as "poor" humans. Some poor humans decide that they have had enough of struggling so they start to try and get money by other means which I will show about below. But first I need to tell you how this dependence by the humans on money came about. It is quite unbelievable to us who do not have this concept of money on our planet.

The Origin of Money

In the earliest times human beings were able to live together in perfect harmony and were able to share all of the Earth's resources freely. They realised that whatever was on the Earth was for everybody. Of course, each individual had different gifts and skills which were given to them to benefit all humankind. Humans were happy to give, rather than to take and gained much joy whenever they created something out of the Earth's natural resources. They also took freely from the Earth all sorts of food which was growing out of the ground and used things like stone and wood which also came from the ground.

Then one day as a result of the Change, someone somewhere decided that they would like to have something that they didn't have the skills to produce themselves. Rather than give this item freely as in the past, the maker wanted the asker to give him something in exchange for it. So, the notion of "trade" was born. This idea of swapping something for something else was quite harmless in itself, but it had the potential to cause great upset if one of the parties didn't think that it was "fair exchange". Thus, humans went on for many centuries living in harmony and sharing and exchanging the earth's resources in all their various forms.

Then eventually another individual had the idea of instead of exchanging something they had created from the Earth for something else, they would swap a "token". This did not have any use for the receiver other than the giver said it was worth the same value as the item he was exchanging. Although the receiver was quite sceptical at first, he still went ahead and exchanged his goods, believing that he would be able to exchange this "currency" for some other goods in the future. This it went on and on until the currency changed into pieces of metal and eventually paper which said that it was worth so much to the possessor. So, the notion of money was born.

All over the Earth money started being produced, with stronger and less scrupulous humans started taking advantage of the weaker and more honest humans. They created more and more of this money. Sometimes it was created by governments, sometimes it was created by individuals. Eventually the notion of "rich" and "poor" came into people's understanding of how the system worked. This was because some humans had a lot of money and most of the rest had very little money.

Naturally, those who had most of the money became powerful, not just in an economic sense, but also in a mindful sense. Those with little money started being exploited by the rich and would gladly sacrifice their individuality and sense of worth in order to gain just a little amount of money from the rich and powerful human beings. They would do any type of job for them, whatever the personal cost. In fact, they became what you would call "slaves" just in order to have enough food to eat, or to have shelter from the elements. So now the rich seem to be getting richer and the poor seem to be getting poorer.

The other major problem with money was that many humans decided that they would like more of this money and although this group of humans didn't attack and hurt other humans directly to get more of this money, they did do a great deal of damage to the planet by their actions. For example, some humans found out that they could take naturally growing things like fruits and vegetables and not share them but sell them to make more of this money for themselves. Others chopped down wood to build houses and furniture but didn't re-plant saplings to replace the trees they had destroyed. Soon whole forests were being cut down, even though many people cried out that this was hurting the planet. Other humans actually burnt down whole forests and the smoke it gave off caused a barrier to form between the sun and the planet and so the Earth warmed up more and more. These people were no different than the criminals that I mentioned earlier because they were hurting other humans by their greed to get more money.

Now I will show you how most humans spend the majority of their time on Earth It is done so that they can get money and is an activity called "work". It is the main way that they receive money.

Work and jobs

Location - Kent, England: the car park of a suburban railway station

William Knowles parked his Mercedes in his reserved space in the station car park as he had done thousands of times before. He quickly looked in the rear-view mirror to check that his tie was straight and his hair looked neat. Then he picked up his copy of his daily newspaper and his briefcase, before locking his car. He then walked the short distance through the car park to the station entrance. He bounced up the steps into the booking hall and opened his wallet, pulling out his annual season ticket, which he touched in at the ticket barrier. As he packed away his ticket and walked through the barrier, he was joined by scores of other commuters all doing the same thing. Then he walked down the steps and onto the platform, just as

*the 8.08 train for London Bridge was arriving. He stepped
into the third carriage of twelve and sat in his usual seat by
the window and opened his newspaper.*

*Thirty minutes later he folded his newspaper and stood up
with dozens of his fellow passengers and got off the train at
platform 4 of London Bridge station. He then walked along the
platform, down the steps and out through the ticket barrier
and turned right going along the underground passage into
the busy London street. He walked across London Bridge with
St Paul's Cathedral on his left and Tower Bridge on his right.
In less than ten minutes he was in his office in the City of
London, sat in front of his computer screen, working in his
office, doing his job, just as he'd done for the past thirty years.*

*He then worked for the next eight hours, which included two
fifteen minute tea breaks and an hour's lunch break. At
precisely 5.00pm he turned off his computer, packed his
briefcase, picked up his umbrella and coat and made his way
back across London Bridge towards London Bridge railway
station where he caught the 17.25 train back to his home
station. He then walked back through the station car park, got
into his Mercedes and drove to his home just he'd done for the
past thirty years.*

The main activity for humans is not enjoying being on the
Earth as you would think. This activity is only practised by
just some of them, who have become enlightened as to their
purpose for being there. Rather the main activity for most
humans is an activity called "working" or "going to work".
This is also known as "having a job", or "being employed", or
sometimes "making a living". It is all tied to the need for
humans to get money, so that they can pay for things that they
need and often things that they do not need. The idea of work
is to do different activities for a master or employer for
payment of money. I know it seems strange to your non-
human brain, but this is what humans have done for eons.

There are many human beings who have to go to work for
another human being or do some type of work for themselves
as they need to make a living as they say. This means that they
do a task each day and trust that another human being will pay
them some money in exchange for the work that they do.

In this activity a human is "employed" by another human to do the work for them, as in the event-capture above. The way he travels to his place of work, first by driving to the station in his car and then taking a train into the city known as London is called "commuting". Billions of humans do this activity day in and day out, all over the planet. They do it for the majority of their time on Earth and then eventually they stop doing this work, either because they have "retired" from their job of work, or because they have simply ended their time on Earth.

Most of the money they earn is spent paying bills for receiving energy to heat and light their homes, and to pay for food to eat so that they can survive physically on Earth. Humans also have to pay some of their money to government of their country in a form called "taxes". This is when the government receives money from all the humans working in a country. It then uses this money to pay for various things like helping poor humans, paying for places that help heal humans who are ill or need their bodies mending, making sure the country is protected and many other things. When a human has paid all these things they may have some money left over which they can spend on things that they choose. I will now tell you about this activity.

Shopping

One of the places that humans go to where they spend their money is called a "shop" and these shops are found all over the planet. They are places filled with goods that the humans choose to buy. Here is an example of a shop.

Location – Miami, Florida, USA: a shopping mall

Lucy Knowles had been sleeping on and off in the queue outside shopping mall. She was waiting with hundreds of other keen shoppers to get some bargains on Black Friday at several large department stores within the mall. She had gone into work as usual on the Thursday but as soon as she had got home, she'd literally dropped her work clothes, changed and grabbed a cheap sleeping bag and some sandwiches and gone to stake her place in the queue.

Everybody seemed to be in quite a jovial mood, though she realised that some of these people could become her enemy in an instant if they wanted to buy what she wanted as well. By about 5.00am people were stating to stir and conversations were starting up as the bargain hunters began to feel excited as the 7.00am opening time approached.

With half an hour to go Lucy was getting agitated. Would she be able to get one of the five silver brooches which the jewellery shop had put on sale for just & $8.99 as opposed to the normal $89.99. By ten to seven everyone was pushed up against the doors looking into the mall where several security guards were standing poised to deal with any trouble makes.

Bang on 7 o'clock a klaxon sounded and the security guards opened the doors. It was an immediate stampede and she found herself being swept along with the others into the mall......

In this event-capture you can see humans waiting to enter a shop to buy some goods. The shops are deliberately designed so that you can see into them easily. This is to show what is inside them as the human beings have a penchant for collecting things as I have already told you. They are often full of colourful human made objects including clothes, which in some cases they don't really need. Of course, some objects in these shops are necessary for human existence such as food and objects that hold their house together. But in most cases the objects in these shops have no human worth at all, save to pacify the human beings' need for possessions.

In the past there used to be a time when humans went shopping for food from a shop very near to their homes. They would walk there and then carry the food home themselves. Then one day one human had the idea of building a very big shop where many different kinds of food goods could be bought for less money than the smaller food shops. They were given the name "supermarkets" as they were much larger than the old types of shops or markets. They were very popular with the humans and they spent more money here than they used to.

Eventually more and more of these supermarkets were created, and soon they became so large that they had to be built on the edge of the towns where the humans lived. This meant that they were too far away from the human's homes to walk there and so the humans needed to get there in their vehicles, which also multiplied. Now the vast majority of human beings in many parts of the world get their food energy and other goods for their houses from these supermarkets, rather than going to the smaller local food shops. The result is that many of these smaller shops have closed as they cannot attract humans to buy their food from them anymore.

There now follows an example of how some humans take money from other humans that isn't theirs and cause all sorts of negative reactions.

Fraud

Location - Gibraltar: a victim of fraud

Stewart Richardson had just got into bed and was about to put out the light when his phone rang. It was just after 11.30 pm and he was very tired after going out for a drink with his mates straight after work. All that alcohol had gone to his head and he knew the moment his head touched the pillow he would be sleeping like a baby.
"Mr. Richardson?" enquired the tough, female voice at the other end of the telephone.
"Who is this?", replied Stewart suspiciously.
"This is Anna Welch from the fraud department of your bank. I need to go over some security details with you before I can let you know why I'm calling".
Stewart gave the necessary information to the caller and then she said, "You haven't been to Egypt in the last two days?"
"No, why?" There have been two withdrawals from your account of approximately £300 and £400". Stewart was shocked and sat down on the bed. "You mean that I've been a victim of Identity Fraud?"

"Yes. It seems that way, Mr Richardson. I see from your records that you made a transaction of £46.50 at a petrol station on the 16th. We believe that your pin may have been taken by a hidden camera when you made that transaction".

"What about my money? That's seven hundred quid gone just like that!"

"Don't worry, Mr Richardson. The money will be refunded in full. We will also send you a new credit card. In the meantime, your current credit card will be frozen to stop anymore transactions. We are sorry for this inconvenience, but you do appreciate that we have to do this to stop anymore fraud on your account from happening".

Stewart switched off his phone and a thousand thoughts went through his head – Who are the people who did this to me? Will they get caught? How many other people have they done this to? When's all this going to end? He then made a vow. "From now on I'll make sure I cover the keyboard with my hand whenever I use my card". But he could not go to sleep in spite of all the alcohol he had drunk. His mind was in a turmoil. His faith in Humanity had just taken a large dip.

Here is an example of two groups of humans and money, with one taking money from the other. The individual has had some money stolen from his bank account by thieves. The thieves have just managed to get money from an innocent human who didn't even know they were doing it. This is one major problem with money when it is used as numbers in a computer in this way. If it was cash money the individual would have either had it in his possession, or it would have been locked away in a bank. Now in the present era of human beings on Earth, money has become a set of numbers inside a computer programme. As a result, it is much easier to steal if someone can "hack" or break into the computer system of a bank.

More and more humans are starting to try and get money from the innocent human beings by pretending they are calling this human from a bank. They say that the human needs to transfer money from his or her account for safety reasons. As the human trusts them and believes they are ringing from a bank he will transfer the money so these other humans steal money from the human. The result is that this human is very unhappy and upset by all this and in some cases can lose a lot of money to these thieves. This is partly because money is now "paperless" as the humans say and just a set of numbers on a computer screen. It is also partly due to the banks choosing to allow this "paperless" money to take over.

Now it is time to show you another way of how humans spend their money. They do this in the hope of getting more money than they actually have.

Gambling

Location - Las Vegas, USA: a gambling room in a large hotel

It was just after ten o'clock in the morning when Marjorie left her hotel room and took the elevator down to the ground floor. She went straight into the gaming room and walked up to the exchange desk, where she handed over a five hundred dollar note to be exchanged for its equivalent in gambling tokens.

She quickly scooped up all the tokens into her small handbag and in no time at all she was sitting in front of a brightly coloured slot machine. The chink, chink of coins being dropped into slot machine could be heard all around the vast room.

She put in three of the tokens in swift succession and watched the three dials spin round and round, until one by one they stopped. They showed two strawberries and an orange. Not good enough to win anything. She then pressed a button and the dial spun around again. This time there was just one each of a lemon, an orange and a strawberry. No win. She tried again and it was the same with three different fruits. She put more tokens in the machine and waited for the wheels to spin.

The machine was taking in more tokens than Marjorie was putting in, Little by little her five hundred dollars was dwindling away.

Another strange human activity is the one known as "gambling". This involves the exchange of money and is when one human being makes a guess about what will happen in an event, usually, a sport. Most of the time this will involve a race involving animals, where the human will guess which horse or greyhound will come first. They will place a "bet" or amount of money on this horse. If this horse wins they will be given more money back than they handed over. But if their horse does not win they will lose that money and the person they gave it to will keep it. The chances of a horse winning a race are called the "odds" and this figure is determined by the "bookie" who must pay out if the horse wins. Usually, a lot of humans place money on the horses that don't win and the bookie keeps all their money and eventually becomes rich in human money terms.

At other places humans place money or tokens in bright, colourful machines which display random pictures as in the event-capture here. They have to wait and see whether three of same type of picture appears in front of them. If it does they will win some money or tokens, if it doesn't they will lose the money that they put into the machine.

The problem with gambling is that many humans become addicted to it and can't stop themselves from betting away their money. They believe that they will win a large amount and will be able to stop gambling for good, but in their reality this never happens and they keep losing all their money. It is the excitement of who will win which gets them hooked, but usually most humans who bet lose money, rather than get more money. But this can lead to them being in a situation where they do not have any money left. In fact, they have borrowed so much money from other people that they have no money left to pay that person or organisation back. This leads to being in a situation called "being in debt". Let me show how this works in the next event-capture.

Debt

Location – Pretoria, South Africa: a semi-detached suburban house

Simon was just about to leave his house to go to work when the post arrived. He picked it up off the doormat and looked at

the post. There was a letter for his wife and two official looking ones for him. He saw one was from the local council and the other one was from his credit card company. His heart sank. He'd been dreading this moment. Much against his better judgement he started to open the envelope. He should have left opening the post until he got home that evening, but his curiosity got the better of him.

As he looked through the list of items on the credit card statement, his heart sank even more. Interest charge: $145.00. Late payment charge: $35.00. Minimum payment: $235.00. There was no way that he could afford to pay this he thought. How on earth could the banks get away with charging so much interest? He was struggling to pay his mortgage and local taxes, let alone pay for food and all the energy bills. What was he going to do? If he told his wife, she'd go ballistic. They always had rows over money, yet it was her spending on the credit card which had got them into this mess. He wiped the sweat off his brow and folded the statement up, before placing it into his jacket pocket. Now he would be late for work and it would play on his mind all day. What on earth was he going to do?

One of the main problems with the human invention called money is that just a small number of human beings possess the majority of the money that there is on Earth. These humans are rich, whilst the rest of the humans are the poor. Most rich people deposit their money in banks as you saw above. As the banks have a lot of money in them, they are able to control and exploit the poor humans who don't have enough money. As you need money to pay for food and water and other basic human necessities, the poor are at the mercy of the banks.

One of the ways in which the banks are able to do this is by giving money to the poor. You would think that they are helping the poor humans by doing this, but in fact they are not. Once they give this money to the poor, they will expect the poor to pay it back to them in the future. This is called "lending" and "borrowing". The bank lends the money to the poor human who is borrowing it from them. As the poor human hasn't got enough money to pay the bank back, he is charged "interest" by the bank. This means that the poor human must pay even more money back to the bank that he borrowed from in the first place. So, in human terms he has got into "debt" with the bank, just like the male human in the scene I have just shown you. This notion of being in debt causes much internal distress for millions of human beings who simply haven't got the money to pay back the bank.

Apart from the banks' lending money to poor people, some individual humans, known as "loan sharks", do the same thing, but charge even more interest than the banks and then the poor humans are in even greater debt. If the poor humans cannot afford the money to these humans back they might start to be violent towards them or take away other objects that they own from their houses. So many humans just become poorer and poorer and start to be depressed about their lives and the way the world is run.

Not only can individual human beings get into debt, but also whole countries can too. They borrow money to pay for goods from other countries or from banks who have a lot of money. Then sometime in the future they are expected to pay it back, yet some of the time the country just hasn't got this money to pay back to the lender and they too get into debt. As a result of this many of the humans in this country suffer in a variety of ways. There might not be many jobs as the country has no money to pay their workers. So many humans in these countries end up living in "poverty" as it is called. Let me show you what this is like.

Poverty

Location - Freetown, Sierra Leone: a rubbish dump on the edge of the city

It was just after 6.00am when Alisha left her home and walked the mile or so to the municipal rubbish tip just outside the centre of Freetown. Walking gingerly over the flesh-tearing broken glass and tins with jagged edges, she made her way through the boggy surface to the large lorries which were starting to unload the last collection of yesterday's rubbish. She knew the saying "the early bird catches the worm", so it was worth getting up early to beat the dozens of other scavengers to get the best pickings from the refuse lorries. Usually, she collected plastic bottles and empty food containers in a large sack provided by her gang master. If she was lucky she might spot a ring or necklace that some rich person had accidentally dropped, but that was once in a blue moon.

If only she had shoes which would give her protection from the frequent cuts and pricks she received as she sifted through the mess. She could also do with a face mask to protect her from the flies and stench that such a large waste tip gave off, but that would never happen. Her main concern was finding enough plastic bottles in the blackened swamp of rubbish, so she could buy her family some flour and fruit so they could eat today. But it was always the gang masters who creamed off the profits for themselves.

Many humans all over the world live in poverty. This means that they do have any money at all, or very little and they are forced to try and do very simple jobs to get some money to buy food. In this event-capture the woman is working on a rubbish dump looking for plastic bottles to sell to another human who will give her some money for the ones she has gathered.

They live like this as they cannot get support from the humans in charge of the country that they live in. This might be because the humans who are in charge do not care for them and spend the money they have on themselves or their friends. Or it might be that the country itself does not have much money itself and cannot afford to help humans like this. In fact, some countries are also poor when compared to other countries who are rich. They too need help from the richer countries, but this does not happen much. It is called "aid" by the humans and only when there is a huge need for help do the richer countries decide to help them.

The answer to this problem seems to be that all countries should come together to help the poorer countries and use some of the money they have to help these poor countries.

When someone becomes so poor because they haven't got any money at all they can quite easily lose the home they live in. It might be through debt, or it might be because they have other problems that they can't solve by themselves and they end up living on the street. Here is an example.

Homelessness

Location - Belgrade, Serbia: a homeless person begging on the street

Stefan coughed and spluttered as he tried to clear his sore throat. He kept repeating the mantra "Got any spare change mate?" to any man, woman or child walking past him. Most of them looked away as they went past. One or two looked him in the eye and then shook their heads as if saying, "No way would I give you any of my hard earned money, scum!" Very occasionally, some kind people would put some money in his cracked and dirty white, plastic cup. Even then it never amounted to much. But something was better than nothing.
Once in a while a kind human might offer him some food. It might be a sandwich, an apple or a chocolate bar. That was useful as he was usually feeling hungry. Sitting for long periods on the hard concrete pavement had left him with sores on his bottom and he often had to stand to ease the pain in his bones. The nights were worst as he slept intermittently. He would have just nodded off when he would be woken by a car or motor bike revving up. Or a police car with its siren blaring out would act as an alarm clock going off, usually at 2 o'clock in the morning. He always tried to find a spot away from the roads as some drunken yob would show absolutely no respect to him and in the past he had been spat on. In one extreme instance he was urinated on by someone who didn't realise he was a human being sleeping there. Or perhaps he did and was being cruel.

In the above event-capture you can see a human that is living on the streets as he is what humans call "homeless". That means that he does not have a home to live in like most human beings. This happens for a number of reasons, but the main one is that he has no money left to live with and now has to resort to "begging" or asking for money from passers-by. It might be that he has no home because he has got into debt like the other human in the earlier event-capture. Or it might be that his relationship with another human has stopped and he can no longer live in the same house as them. Or it might be that he has become addicted to drinking alcohol or taking drugs. Or it might be a combination of all three reasons.

The human seems to have been forgotten about by the humans in charge of the country he lives in and as some humans describe his case, he has "slipped through the net". There are some humans who help these homeless humans though, as they care for them and so there is hope for him. But there seem to be so many humans like this about in all places around the world in spite of all the money there is in the world.

Many humans do care about humans like this and they form into special groups of humans called "charities". These groups exist to help all sorts of humans who need help and they only exist because other humans give them money to do so. Here is an example of how some charities work.

Charities

Location – Syria: a refugee camp

There were tents for as far as the eye could see. All providing a "temporary" home to the tens of thousands of refugees who had lost their homes through all the shelling and bombing in the war. Some families had been here for over five years and it looked like they may have to stay there for at least another five years. A few of the children playing on the dusty streets had actually been born here and knew no other life.
Two aid workers from one of the several charities based here were making their daily rounds around the camp. Although there were no formal street names for the many lanes in the camp, they knew each lane by a certain name given to it by the

*residents, such as "Long Street" or "Peace Alley". They
checked on certain tents where they knew one or more of the
residents had been ill. Sometimes it might be influenza, other
times smallpox. They handed out precious medicines that were
needed as there were no pharmacies or hospitals in a place
like this.*

*Over in a corrugated iron compound on the other side of the
camp a female doctor from another charity was making her
weekly checks on the many pregnant women living here. Her
days were long and hard, such was the demand. She was
always exhausted at the end of the day, yet she felt a
tremendous feeling of peace, knowing that she was making a
difference to these people's lives, however small that may be.*

In this event-capture you can see some humans from different
charities helping other humans who need help. These humans
work for charities that have been formed by one human being
or by groups of humans why choose to help other humans
who are suffering in some way. This is similar to what
governments in countries do, except that many governments
choose not to help people in need, as they spend the money
they receive from taxes on other things. Thus, other humans
who can see a need to help humans start up these charities to
help them.

Charities could be helping humans who have a physical or a
mental need; or they might be helping animals in some way;
or they could be helping to save a human creation from
destruction. For these charities to exist, they need to have
money coming into to them from other humans. As the
governments don't give the charities this money, they instead
ask other humans to give them money.

Humans love generating money for the charities by doing all
sorts of strange things. For instance, they might walk or swim
or run a certain distance and then get other humans to give
them money for doing this. Or they might do something to
their bodies, like cut off the hair on their heads, or wear some
funny clothing, or do something unpleasant to themselves, all
so that they can get other people to give them money.

Part 10

Human Leisure

A man must break his back to earn his day of leisure

Leisure Time

When human beings manage to break themselves free of their activity called working, they have what they call "leisure time", where they are free to relax and actually be themselves. As I mentioned earlier the humans have a peculiar system of behaviour called "free choice" where they are able to choose what to say, do or think. It is when the humans are in this state of leisure that they seem to be happiest. Yet the ironic thing is that in order to achieve this state, virtually every human being has to go through the toil of work and money accumulation first.

There are many different things that the humans do in this leisure state and in this part of my report I will show you some of the most important as far as the humans are concerned.

Holidays

Humans have not always had the event known as "holidays" in their lives. It was only introduced into their lives in recent times and is understood to be having time off or a break from their work pursuits. Most of the time this means "going on holiday" or going to live in a different part of the Earth for a short period of time as part of their leisure pursuits. For some humans it means just staying in their homes and not having to go to work. Here is an example of human beings on holiday.

Location – a British seaside holiday resort in the summer

The promenade was busy with holiday crowds walking along it in both directions. Many of them were admiring the view out to sea, with a wide sandy beach just below them. It was a glorious day with not a cloud in the sky, with the sun shining down on the scene. Many families had come to this seaside resort for their annual summer holiday just as their parents and their grandparents had done so years before. Ice cream kiosks were doing a good trade, as were the many souvenir shops dotted along the promenade, selling everything from candy floss and sticks of rock through to fridge magnets and tacky postcards.
Down on the beach young children were holding onto the hands of their parents as they paddled in the cold sea. They jumped up as the waves broke over their tiny bodies, screaming with delight. Further out away from all the melee a group of teenagers were larking around on airbeds and rafts. A couple of lifeguards kept an eye on things, making sure that everyone was looked after and protected.
On the nearby pier, crowds walked up and down, some watching the scene on the beach, some having a go on the many penny slot machines dotted here and there. Right at the end of the pier several fishermen were trying their luck at catching the fish that were swimming between the rusting cast-iron pillars.

From the above event-capture you see humans on holiday. In this case they have gone on holiday to the "coast", where the land meets the sea. This is because many humans do not live near the sea and enjoy visiting it to swim in it or just lay on the sand next to the sea "sunbathing". This is when humans sit or lie down so the rays of the sun can warm their bodies up with its heat. It can be a dangerous thing to do as some humans can get burnt by the rays of the sun and so can get ill because of it. For many years humans is not just going to stay at a place where there is a beach. Many humans prefer to go to places inland, away from the sea as well. They like instead to learn and experience how different humans live and exist in different parts of the planet. They might even decide to live there instead of their original country as they like it so much. As I have shown you in the Human Movement section they can travel to these places in various human forms of transport such as aeroplane, boat, train or car.

Hobbies

Most humans use a lot of their free time away from working doing an activity known as having a "hobby". This means doing an activity that they are very interested in and enjoy doing as it makes them both happy and relaxed. There are myriads of hobbies that the humans practise and I will show you just one of these hobbies now.

Location – The Lowlands of Scotland: a father and son fishing by the side of a river

It had been a slow day for Ian and his son, Jake. They had been fishing for over four hours now and had only caught three fish between them, a couple of carp and a bream. Ian had been taught the hobby by his father, and now he was passing it on to his son. Jake enjoyed going out for the day, fishing with his father every so often, but did find it boring at times and probably spent more time on his mobile phone playing games rather than actually watching the water, in case there was a bite.
Ian, on the other hand enjoyed his hobby tremendously. It was all he lived for - apart from his family - and when he was at work he would often day dream that he was sitting on the river bank, rod in hand, waiting for his float to twitch. He had spent a fortune on his hobby over the years, but he thought it was money well spent. It brought him so much pleasure.
"Dad!" called Jake. "Look! There's something pulling".
Jake's fishing line had become taut and it was starting to move. Ian instinctively grabbed Jake's rod and started reeling the line in.

"This is something big!" he said excitedly.
The fish on the other end of the line was struggling and was
suddenly lifted up out of the water and dropped into the net
that was situated right next to the riverbank.
"It's a Pike, Dad!" shouted Jake excitedly.
"Well, I haven't caught one of these for years. Well done,
son!" Ian said.
"It had been worthwhile after all", he thought.

This event-capture is showing you one human hobby which
you may find quite strange which is called, "fishing". It is
usually practised by the male of the human species and can
take up much of their human time. It involves sitting for long
periods by some water, either a river, stream, canal, lake or in
some cases the open sea. They dangle a long piece of wood or
metal over the water. Attached to this is a length of thin
material which is called a "line". On the end of the line is a
metal hook with food or "bait" attached to it. The person
fishing then waits until a fish comes along and bites at the
food, but at the same time the hook will get attached to its
mouth and the fisherman will then pull it out of the water,
having "caught" this fish.
Sometimes the fisherman will keep the fish and take it to his
home for food. At other times the fish caught will be kept in a
net in the water and then released when the fisherman has
finished his time by the water. This activity is done for "fun"
or enjoyment by many humans as a hobby. It is different from
the other type of fishing where humans go out to sea in boats
of differing sizes to catch fish. This time they are trying to
catch lots of fish in large nets as opposed to just one on a
fishing line. The object of this activity is to catch lots of
different kinds of fish and other types of sea creatures, and
then sell then for money to other humans who want these fish
for a source of their food.
Fishing is just one hobby that the humans enjoy doing. There
are so many different types of hobby that the humans do that I
cannot possibly list them all here. But here are some of the
most popular ones:- mending cars, painting, knitting, writing,
making pottery, drawing, photography, doing jigsaws,
cooking, doing puzzles, collecting stamps, running, doing

sports, model making, DIY, flower pressing, doing crosswords, making films, learning to play a musical instrument, listening to music, making clothes.

Some hobbies involve an activity known as "collecting". This is done by both old and young humans. Let me show you an example of this in action.

Collecting things

Location - Corinth, Greece: inside a terraced house

The two brothers were eagerly anticipating the weekly visit of their grandparents, Michail and Vasia. As the minutes passed by, they grew more excited, wondering how much longer they would be. Christos, aged ten and Asterios, aged eight had their football card book open and each had a piece of paper on which they had written the names of the footballers they still needed the cards for. It would be a while before they would complete the set, but it was the joy of opening a new packet and seeing which cards were in it which they seemed to enjoy the most.

"Hello boys!" boomed Grandad Michail as he entered the room.

"Lovely to see you two again", said Grandma Vasia as she bent down to kiss the two grandchildren.

The boys hugged the two grandparents in response and then stood there anticipating what would come next.

"Waiting for something?" teased their grandfather.

The boys looked at him expectantly. Grandma Vasia giggled.

Then their grandfather pulled four packets of the cards that they so desperately wanted from his pocket.

Both boys ruched to grab the cards, but their Grandad was too quick and lifted them into the air. Slowly he lowered his arm down and said, "Well?"

The boys knew what to say and offered a "Thank you" each before being handed the cards.

They ripped the packets open and started looking at the contents.

"Got. Not got", they said in unison as they sorted the cards into two piles, ready to add the new ones to the ever-increasing collections.

Many humans love to have objects which they call their "possessions". They want these possessions and "collect" or gather them, so that they now "belong" to them. Ever since the humans used to collect nuts and berries from the trees and bushes in their earliest days of existence on Planet Earth, they have continued this practice. Whether it is a an old or a young human, they still continue to do this. It seems that human beings take great joy in collecting objects whether they be pieces of metal or pottery, paintings, books, dolls, toys, antiques and so on.

In fact, it is possible to collect just about anything that exists on Planet Earth. It can either be a natural object which has been formed on the planet such as a piece of rock, or a crystal, or even something living like animals. Or it can be something created by the humans, which is "man-made" such as jewellery, clothing, or music in its various forms.

When the humans start collecting something, they find that they need more and more of whatever they are collecting. So, to do this they use their money to pay for new items to add to their collection. In some cases, they become so obsessed with adding different objects to their collections that they become addicted to the desire to have more and more of these objects. In other words, they just cannot give up what they are collecting, as chasing after the object and then eventually getting this object makes them feel particularly happy.

There are other humans who don't collect objects though. They collect "experiences" instead. These are really the action of doing something which they enjoy so much that they keep doing this experience. It might be visiting certain places on the planet, or doing something which they find quite fearful, but which makes them feel very happy, or it might be the action of jumping from a great height down towards a river, only to be stopped by the rope that is attached to them.

Again, if the human collecting these experiences keeps having them, they too can become addicted to this collecting and want more and more of this experience until it takes over their lives and stops them living a normal, balanced life.

Now, I will show you some leisure practices that go under the term of "entertainment".

Entertainment

The human notion called "entertainment" is where the human being forgets about themselves and what they are doing on Planet Earth. Instead, they let their minds be "entertained" by outside forces. This means other humans doing something with their bodies or voices which gains their attention for a certain amount of human time These can be all sorts of different things, such as an audio activity like listening to music or someone reading them a story; or a visual activity such as watching television, film or sport.
Humans want to be entertained as it their way of escaping from their normal lives. This entertainment activity has the effect of taking the humans "out of themselves". In other words, they no longer become aware of themselves as humans, but are in fact focussed on other humans doing this entertainment. In many cases they become obsessed with what the other humans are doing, especially with sport. Here, certain human emotions take over their brain function, which they would not normally use in their everyday lives. These emotions might be anger or pleasure or hatred or love for example.

I will now go into more detail about how the humans entertain themselves.

Watching Television

Here is an example of someone being entertained by what comes out of a television set.

Location - Edinburgh, Scotland: the living room of a tenement house

The middle aged woman sat down in her favourite chair and lit a cigarette. She looked eagerly at the TV set a few feet away from her. The theme music for her favourite soap opera had just started and she couldn't wait to see what would happen in today's episode. Her daughter walked past her and into the kitchen, but she hardly noticed her.
The opening scene continued from last night's episode where Steve Grainger had been in bed with his mistress, Julia Webb, and Steve's wife, Rosemary had walked in.
"I suppose you've got an excuse for this?" she shouted at Steve. "Just like all the other ones you've had in the past!"
Steve feebly replied, "I can explain", whilst Julia held the bed sheet tighter against her, as her heart pounded with fear.
"It's not what it seems" said Steve. Rosemary, red with rage, grabbed a vase of flowers and poured its contents right over Julia, who screamed.
The woman, watching this scene unfold, gasped in shock at the scene being played out on the box in front of her, as though it were happening in her own bedroom. She was definitely on Rosie's side and hoped that Steve would get his come-uppance.
"Go on Rosie! Sort that bastard Steve out!" she shouted at the TV.
Just as it was about to get even more intense, the Soap Opera shifted to a different scene and the woman groaned with annoyance.

You see here a scene which is played out all over the Earth in millions of homes: a human being watching the box-like object called a television set. At first programmes were transmitted during the evening. But now they are shown at all times of the day and night. So, if people can't sleep they can watch the television. They also have many, many different channels which show different types of programmes. These could be about what is happening in different parts of the world, which they call "the news". Or it could be an entertainment programme where some humans sing or dance or tell jokes to an audience. Or it could be a drama programme where various human beings pretend that they are other human beings acting out different human events, as you are seeing here. Or it could be a sports programme where humans are competing against each other to win a game of something.

The thing is that all humans like to watch television programmes, as it takes them away from their normal lives where they are working to get money. It helps them to forget about this drudgery and it can take over the human's lives in some instances. They become obsessed with having to watch a certain programme – quite often a soap opera as in this case – and they need to know what is happening to the humans in this pretend human world. Some even believe that it is real and fail to see the humans in it as merely actors pretending to be someone else!

It is not just the adult humans who let the television take over their lives, but also the younger humans as well. If they can't watch a programme they wanted to see, they can get angry or miserable. In many cases they will just sit on a chair or lie on a bed watching the television instead of playing outside with their friends, or reading a book, or just talking with other human beings.

I have already told you about the human activity called sport. As I have said sport can take many forms, but basically it is a game where two groups of humans or two individual humans try to achieve something before the other human can do so. This activity is not only very popular with those who take part in the sport, but also with the humans who like to observe it taking place. In fact, it is so popular that millions of human beings are watching it all over the world. Let me show you this in action.

Watching Sport

Location – A football match at an English football ground

The forward received the ball just outside the penalty area and managed to swerve past two defenders. Now all he had to

*do was beat the goalkeeper. It looked like his debut goal for
his new club was about to happen. He shot, but the ball went
searing over the goal and into the back of the stand holding
the away fans.*

*"You're not fit.... You're not fit.... You're not fit to wear the
shirt" chanted the group of home fans behind the goal at the
opposite end. They were venting their fury at their club's latest
signing, Sergio Mendini, a twenty million pound signing from
one of the top Italian clubs. He'd been at his new club for
nearly a month and had yet to score. Now there was a growing
group of fans who could only see the folly of their manager in
shelling out such a large amount of money for no return.*

*"You're just scum!" shouted one of the ringleaders of the
singing group of home fans" Others started chanting, "What a
waste of money! What a waste of money!"*

*Meanwhile one of the home team's wingers had swept up the
right wing and was passing the ball across the goalmouth and
into the box. The new signing jumped high and his head
connected with the ball at just the right moment. Wham! The
ball went rocketing past the goalkeeper and into the back of
the net. The home fans jumped up in glee and cheered one of
their loudest cheers for many a game. "Sergio is magic.
Sergio is magic!" they chanted in unison. Their hatred and
contempt for him had turned to admiration in a matter of
seconds.*

In the event capture here, you can see an example of one type
of sport taking place. The activity of sports may seem strange
to you on our planet, but many millions of humans love to
watch these sports activities taking place. The event-capture
above is showing a sport called "football", which is sometimes
known as "soccer" and it involves two different groupings of
humans kicking a ball with their feet. One group tries to kick
the ball into a particular area of the place where they are
playing this game, whilst the other group or "team" tries to
stop them from doing so. Whoever has the ball in their
possession is called the "attackers", whilst those trying to stop
them and get the ball from them are called the "defenders".
All the time many humans are at the sides of the "pitch" or
area they are playing in, shouting and singing. These humans

are called "fanatics", or "fans" for short. When one side, or one individual human manages to place the ball in the area which is called a "goal", they have now "scored" a goal. As a result of this, the group of humans watching this happen shout and cheer and jump up and down and hit their hands together because they are very happy that this has happened. At the same time the group of humans following the other team remain silent and get upset because they are now losing. This all stops when the game ends and one side has "won" whilst the other side has "lost". Sometimes when no goals are scored, or both sides score the same number of goals, it is called a "draw".

This is just one type of game which involves moving a ball. There are plenty of other sports' games similar to this which have the names of "Rugby", "Cricket", "Hockey", "Golf" and "Tennis". They are all watched by huge numbers of humans all over the planet who can become quite obsessed with following their team or following just one of their players.

Human sport doesn't just involve games with a sphere though. There are many others which involve humans watching humans or animals run in "races" where the winner is the one which is the fastest over a given distance. It can be horse or greyhound racing, or humans running in races over various distances. Sometimes these races can be on snow or ice and involve the humans using the tools of skates or skis. Or in another sport the humans use a vehicle such as a car, bicycle or motorbike to go around a specially built track. Then there are other sports where the human has to be the best at a given sport such as jumping upwards or lengthwise, or throwing a spear or a metal sphere. Finally, there are races which take place on water such as "rowing", "swimming" or "sailing". In fact, there are so many different sports that it would be impossible to list them all here.

Why do the humans bother to do this? you might be asking. In most cases the answer would be that they receive a reward or "prize" for doing this. This may be a metal "cup" or metal "medals" which they wear on their body as a sign that they are the best, or one of the best at a particular sport. In many cases the humans are given money as a prize and if they keep winning at their sport they can accumulate a lot of money.

Finally, they enjoy all the adulation and positive feelings that they receive from their fans.

Apart from watching and taking part in sports the humans also spend a lot of their leisure time playing games by themselves. Here is just one example of this.

Playing games

Location – Santiago, Chile: the bedroom of a teenage boy

Graham was on Mars looking around him at the sandy orange landscape. He turned his head to both left and right and examined the terrain before him. He decided to take a few steps forward and found that everything felt as it was in slow motion. The low lying hills in front of him gradually got nearer, yet he started to lose his breath with the effort. The stars looked very different than on the photos and films he had seem. More bright. More alive than he expected. The high definition TV he had at home was nothing on this. As he walked, he found himself looking down rather than forward as there were a great many holes and cracks in the land. Suddenly he took a step too far and started to fall down a hole that had mysteriously opened up below him. He instinctively raised his arms and made a futile attempt at grabbing an overhead rock to his right but he missed. Next thing he knew he was back down to Earth literally. There he was, lying on the floor of his bedroom with his virtual reality headset on the floor behind him. He has failed miserably in his conquest of Mars!

In this event-capture you are seeing a young human playing a type of game which involves the human invention of "virtual reality". This is where the humans have copied something on Earth that is naturally there and not "man-made". This copy has been put into a computer programme and then inserted into a headset which the human then wears on its head. This headset then produces a physical picture of another place, sometimes on Earth, sometimes on another planet, such as

Mars in this case, or somewhere in the space surrounding the Earth. This picture then "fools" the human brain that he or she is actually in this place when in reality they are in their human home.

The game can be something that is done for fun or "amusement". Or it can be something that is done where one or more human becomes the "winner" and the other human or humans become the "loser". Although the human/s that win, enjoy this feeling of being the winner, those who are the losers do not like this feeling. Yet humans keep on playing games or sports as they like they feeling of winning and being the best at something they have attempted. If they are the loser or lose in a particular game or sport they can become upset and unhappy. If this keeps on happening the humans can become depressed and very unhappy. Yet, many humans keep on playing these games as they think they have to, or because they have become addicted to playing them, just like in any human activity.

The next aspect of human leisure is one which is to do with putting a certain type of liquid into the human body as way of changing the human's perception to the world they are living in. Let me show you.

Drinking Alcohol

Location – Cardiff, Wales: a city centre street early on a Saturday morning *

It was just after 2.00am as Tracey Lewis staggered out of the nightclub, tripping on the pavement curb and fell down into the road. "Tracey! You're well and truly pissed!" shouted her best mate Leanne Booth, chuckling as she extended her hand to lift Tracey to her feet. "Yeah. That was a fucking good night. I've lost count of how many mixers I've had".
As Tracey managed to stand up straight, two males came up to the pair of women and started up a conversation. The taller of the two said "Hello, darlin'" to Tracey and looked her up and down. "You're a well tasty bird". Tracey half heard what he

said, but when he moved his face towards her, she responded without any qualms. Their lips touched and parted as they French kissed. Within a moment the man's hand moved down her back towards her bottom and gave it a gentle squeeze. "Mmm...That's nice" she replied and began to kiss him even more passionately.

Leanne meanwhile had kept her distance from the other man, eying him suspiciously. "You two ladies need a lift?" volunteered the second male. I've got my wheels just round the corner. "No thanks", replied Leanne. "We're getting a cab". "What about you?" said the first male, looking directly into the eyes of Tracey. "Don't waste your time with him!" interrupted Leanne. "He's just after one thing!" but Tracey replied, "So might I be!" "Suit yourself" snapped Leanne, who turned to walk to the taxi rank around the corner. Tracey meanwhile started to walk the other way with both men's arms wrapped round her........

Alcohol is a liquid form of energy which the human beings drink down into their bodies, most of which eventually passes right through the body and back into the Earth. There is one part of it however which goes into the human body's blood and this affects the human's brain. It has the effect of slowing the human's heart down and affecting their brains so that their movements slow down. Plus, they lose control of their senses in some ways in that they do things that they wouldn't do if they hadn't swallowed the alcohol, as you can see in the event-capture above.

When humans take in a lot of this alcohol they become what the humans call "drunk" and the human body does not function as it normally does. If the humans take in very large quantities of it, the effect of the alcohol will eventually cause the human to lose consciousness and fall asleep.

Many humans, especially the young adult humans, like to drink alcohol in large amounts, especially on Friday and Saturday nights in certain parts of the world. They go into their town centres in large numbers and do an activity they call "clubbing". They may dance at these places or just talk to each other, but all the while they are drinking more and more alcohol, until it affects them in the ways I have just described.

Other humans like to go out to drink alcohol in a building where they meet other humans just to talk or watch a television screen. This is known as a "pub", or "public house" or "bar". Again, if the human drinks a lot of alcohol in the pub, they too will get drunk.

The alcohol has various human names, such as "beer", ""wine" or "spirits". It can be any human colour there is, though the majority of human alcohol drinks are yellow or brown. The human beings who drink so much alcohol that it affects their brain, and gets them drunk, can also become quite ill. So much so that they vomit it back up or lose control of their movements, so they fall down onto the ground and hurt their bodies. They can also make negative decisions whilst under the alcohol influence and end up fighting with each other or being taken control of by other humans.

Several hours later when the alcohol has lost its control over the human body they may feel unwell and have a large pain feeling in their brain, which they call a "hangover". Yet this does not seem to put the humans off from drinking more alcohol. In fact, they may well be drinking more alcohol only hours later.

There are some human beings who find that they must drink alcohol every day or every week, or they will not be happy and relaxed. In fact, this becomes an addiction and can make their lives very unhappy. They are known as "alcoholics" by the other humans and find that they cannot stop themselves from having a drink of alcohol, no matter how hard they try. This can lead to all sorts of problems in their lives, such as losing their money, their families or their home. In the end their situation gets worse and worse until they leave their human body, or they manage to overcome this desire for alcohol and start living a normal human life again.

Taking Drugs

Alcohol is just one type of "drug" that the humans put into their bodies as part of their leisure time. Humans also enjoy taking other sorts of drugs as well as a leisure activity. Adult humans ingest these drugs into their bodies in order to facilitate a change within their brains. They do it to get some type of pleasure out of it, or they do it to forget about their human existence and so escape from the hopelessness they feel about being humans. Let me show you what it is like for a human to take in one of these drugs into their body and the effects it has on them.

Location – Basel, Switzerland: a flat on the edge of the city

It was almost an hour since Christian had swallowed the tab. Nothing had happened at first but suddenly his head started pounding and his vision became blurred. He looked out of the window and the blue sky started to change colour to a dark blue and then black. At the same time the white clouds became giant sheep that grew and grew until they were right in front of him. Their eyes stared right into him and their mouths opened as if they were about to eat him. Terrified he turned round and looked into his bedroom. His dark brown wardrobe started to vibrate and he heard deep moaning sounds coming out it. It started to move towards him as if it were about to swallow him.

He closed his eyes in an effort to stop this and he was suddenly flying up into space at such a speed that his knuckles grew white as he gripped his bed sheets. Immediately he was in space looking down on earth and floating helplessly. He started to panic again as he wished he was back down on Earth in his bedroom, but all he could see was the vast darkness of space. Next he saw numerous meteorites coming straight at him. His body dodged each one with a sudden movement to the right and then the left. It was like he was a ten pin at a bowling alley with several balls coming towards him all at once.

With a concentrated effort he shot back to Earth and landed in the sea. This time he was descending down to the very depths of the ocean and could see large grey sharks coming towards him. He knew he had to get away or he would be eaten up by the sharks.

"Help me!" he cried out in his fear. "Aargh!" he screamed in terror. As he did so he felt some warm arms reach around his body. Was it an octopus now? Then he heard a familiar

human voice, "It's OK Christian. I'm here now. I'll protect you and watch over you". Christian recognised it as his girlfriend and straight away the terror feeling left him and a huge feeling of calm descended on him as though a cloud of warm love was engulfing him. He was safe.

As I have just mentioned there are various substances that some human beings put into their bodies with the purpose of changing their emotions and viewpoint on life. These are various chemicals which the humans call "drugs" which alter the brain frequencies so that their view of human reality is altered. They call this getting "high" or "stoned" and sometimes this has the effect of relaxing the human so much that they go to sleep. Since the beginning of human existence on Planet Earth, human beings have been ingesting these drugs, some of which came from plants and some of which in recent times have been manufactured in human laboratories.

They have all sorts of names including, "cannabis", "heroin", "LSD" and "cocaine" and are taken inside the body by more and more humans. The main problem with the drugs is that they can become addictive and so the human who takes them wants to have them more and more. They cannot stop taking them and this has a negative effect on their bodies and especially their brain. The other problem is that they need to pay to have these drugs from humans known as "dealers" and if they become addicted to them they eventually run out of money to pay for them. This leads to violence against the drug user by the dealer and so it only makes the drug users life worse.

One activity connected with drugs that humans do is known as "smoking". This basically means inhaling smoke into the lungs of the human body and then exhaling it out again. Humans do this as they find it helps relax them and keep them calm. Most humans do this through the use of "cigarettes" which are tobacco leaves rolled up into a small tube which is then set alight. Other humans in some parts of the world use a "pipe" with tobacco in it to smoke. When humans want to take some of the above drugs they add it to the tobacco and then inhale its smoke.

Whilst smoking is legal in many countries you are still not allowed to smoke in many places and it is gradually dying out. Instead, many humans are choosing a new alternative called "vaping" where they still inhale a type of smoke but it comes from a liquid in a plastic tube. The humans inhale them vapour from the liquid which can be various flavours and taste nicer than the tobacco in cigarettes.

Many of the drugs that humans take are grown naturally in many countries in very large quantities on land that could be used for growing food crops. Yet because the humans are prepared to pay a lot of money for these drugs, the people who grow them find they get more money from growing the drugs and selling them, than if they grew human food and sold that. This has led to a system called "the drugs trade" where the drugs are grown in one country and then taken over land and sea, or in the air to other countries where other humans will pay a lot of money to have them.

Of course, there are many human beings trying to stop the other humans from growing and taking these drugs, but in the end they find it very difficult to stop every human who wants to take drugs from doing so. In many countries it has led to a lot of human beings being killed by other human beings on both sides.

Here is a completely different human activity that humans do as a leisure activity.

Hunting animals

Location - Namibia, Africa: a game reserve *

The American tourist had waited patiently for this moment. It was extremely hot and uncomfortable for him, having to wait in the open with very little shade for him and his guide. It was irritating him lying flat on his tummy with various insects crawling on him, and flies landing on his face every so often. Eventually, after what seemed an age, an aging male lion came into view about thirty yards in front of the pair. His mane was all tattered with a lifetime of living in the bush and they could see some ribs through their binoculars.

The guide gave the trophy hunter the agreed signal and he took aim. He waited a few seconds so that the lion was standing still then he pressed the trigger on his rifle and waited. The bullet missed its head but went into his flank and straightaway the lion collapsed onto the dry and dusty ground. He was still breathing and fighting to stay alive. The guide stood up and waved at the trophy hunter to follow him. They slowly walked to within twenty feet of the lion. The guide nodded his head and the hunter aimed his rifle once more. The second shot killed the lion stone dead and a great sense of pride filled the mind of the hunter.

He had finally completed the "Big Five". He could now add lion to the elephant, buffalo, rhino and leopard that he had hunted and killed.

In this event-capture you can see an example of a leisure activity that some humans practise called "trophy hunting'. The humans have carried hunting for aeons on the planet as a means of survival. They needed to hunt and kill other animals for food, otherwise they might have starved to death. Gradually over time hunting for survival has decreased so much that only a few small groups of humans practise this activity at the present time. Instead, the humans have developed a method of keeping animals in captivity where they are bred to be used for their food needs. I showed you an event-capture of this in Part 1 of my report. More recently in human time some humans have started to hunt for pleasure using instruments they have invented called "guns" which are able to kill not only animals as in this event-capture, but also other humans as you will have seen elsewhere in this report. This leisure activity of "trophy hunting" is just one aspect of human behaviour where humans have to hunt and kill various animals of varying shapes and sizes. Whilst some humans enjoy doing this activity, there are many more humans who do not agree with it and are trying to stop this from happening.

In the final part of this section of my report I want to show you the opposite of carrying out an activity that happens to some humans. You will find this quite unusual. Let me show you this in action.

Boredom

Location – Tokyo, Japan: a bedroom of a suburban house

The ten year old boy came in from school and went straight into the kitchen. His mum was watching a quiz programme on the TV. She said "Hi. How was your day, Honey?" "OK", replied the boy nonchalantly. He opened the large fridge and helped himself to a coke and a chocolate bar, before leaving the kitchen to go up the stairs to his bedroom. His mother didn't notice him leave as she was engrossed in the TV show.
He opened his bottle of coke, unwrapped the chocolate bar wrapping and flicked on the TV that was at the end of his bed. An ice hockey game flashed up on the screen. He flicked the remote control to the next channel. It was a music channel. He flicked the switch again. It was a news channel. He switched channels once more. This time it was a cartoon. He started watching the TV, but after a minute he flicked the switch again. It was the quiz programme that his mother was watching. He switched channels again and again, but as each programme appeared he thought, "No. I don't like that" or "That's stupid" Eventually, he had flicked through all two hundred and ten channels that were available, but still he hadn't found what he was looking for.
"I'm bored" he thought, as two of his friends rode past his house on their bikes, on the way to the local park to play football.

"Boredom" is a state of mind that many humans have inside themselves when they cannot find anything that they can concentrate their mind on. So far I have shown you a variety of pursuits that humans do which come under the subject of "leisure". With leisure the human mind is stimulated to such a degree that they forget about everything else around them and focus on that one leisure pursuit. As humans call it, they are "in the zone". When they are in this state they enjoy the activity and their brain releases hormones that make them feel happy and fulfilled.

However, there are some humans, particularly the younger ones, who find it difficult to concentrate on a particular leisure pursuit and their mind is in a way empty of any focus. This is known as "boredom" and can take the form of not being able to focus on one particular thing. The human gets frustrated and angry in some cases as they are not contented and relaxed which they would be if they were doing a leisure activity. In the event-capture above the young human cannot settle down into doing one activity. Nothing he looks at on his TV engages his mind. If he were an animal he would probably go to sleep and then wake up and get on with his life. But as he is a human he wants to feed his brain in some way.

In the next part of my report, I will tell you about how some humans use and hurt other humans and the planet to get something that they want, without thinking of the consequences.

Part 11

Human Exploitation

Civilisation is trying to find a new way to die

In this penultimate part of my report, I want to show you how the human beings have been exploiting the planet, from its natural resources and its living things. through to each other. There is much that they have been doing which is both harmful to the planet and to all forms of life on the planet. Let me explain.

Exploitation of the Planet

Ever since humans have been existing on Planet Earth they have exploited the planet for their own needs. Whilst in the early days they used the natural resources of the planet for their basic needs such as food and shelter, they have gradually been exploiting the planet in other ways. This has meant destroying things that can never be replaced. Over the time that humans have lived on Earth, they have destroyed countless animals and water creatures, sometimes for food, sometimes to protect themselves and sometimes through destroying their habitats to make way for human settlements.

They have also been gradually destroying the Earth under their feet by such activities as mining, exploration, testing their weapons and putting their waste there. This has been done mainly to extract certain rocks and minerals that could be made into other things useful to the humans. They have also been taking out of the ground various fossil fuels to heat and power their settlements and industries. This has led to some of the land above the holes they make collapsing and making it dangerous to inhabit. Let me show you how this exploitation has taken place.

Power Sources

Whilst the humans have begun to understand and exploit the energy sources within their own bodies, they seem very primitive when it comes to creating energy for their human needs of heat, light, and power. For eons they used only the very basic elements of fire and water for their power. It is only very recently that they advanced to the stage in their development where they discovered the power of electricity, but they still haven't learnt how to create this with free, renewable energy for everyone.

The first thing you will see is that the humans are using fossil fuels for most of their energy needs, rather than the free energy that is available from their star and from the water and air on their planet. You see they think that the best way they can create electricity is by burning substances taken from inside the ground. These include the fossil fuels of coal, gas and oil. All of these are not able to be recycled once they have been burnt, but turn mostly into carbon, which cannot be used as a power. Let us look first of all at how they are using these fossil fuels. The first one is coal as that has been used the longest of the three I am going to show you.

Coal

Location - near Crackow, Poland: a coal mine

The lift reached the bottom of the mine shaft and seven miners walked out into the artificial light of the mine. Although there was electrical lighting down here, the blackness of the rocks made it still look very dark. Most of the men in the group had been working as miners for over ten years and had become hardened to the conditions and way of life. Yet for one of them, it was only his second week as a miner and he was finding it hard to adjust to life underground. A couple of them joked and laughed as they got into the tiny coal trucks which would take them to the mine face. Ten minutes later they arrived at the end of the line and they stepped out onto the roughly hewn floor. The air down here was much thinner, as it was well away from the mine shaft. The air venting system left a lot to be desired and coughing from the miners was a common occurrence.

After a few minutes' walk, they all arrived at the mine face ready for another hard day's work: drilling and cutting, picking up the coal and loading it into boxes, and then carrying it the short distance to the rail trucks. Eight hours later they would make the return journey back to the mine shaft and then up to daylight.

The hard black substance known as "coal" has been dug out of the ground for thousands of years in a process called "mining". The humans have learnt that if they set the coal on fire and burn it, the heat it gives off can be used to power many things. There was a period in human time known as the "Industrial Revolution" when the use of coal became very popular as it was used to power various industries that started at this time. One of the main uses of coal was to heat water to turn it into steam and then power locomotives and machinery in their factories. This enabled the humans to produce lots and lots of manufactured goods and to travel all over their countries by railways that were powered by steam locomotives.

But as these industries grew, the amount of coal in the ground decreased until in some areas there was no coal left at all. The humans began to realise that the coal gave off a chemical called carbon and this was left all over the Earth as a deposit. It came from the coal in the form of "smoke" which rose into the air, and this would make their buildings and clothes dirty as it landed back on the Earth again. This was known as "pollution" and was also very bad for the humans as they breathed it into their bodies, particularly into their lungs, which gave them various illnesses which made them weak and ill.

Gradually, the humans realised that burning coal was not the best way of creating energy for their needs, especially as it was being used up in many areas so other fossil fuels began to take their place, which you will learn about below.

Oil and gas

Location – Kuwait: an oil refinery

The vast desert sands spread out as far as the eye could see. It was very flat, save for a slight rise in the landscape to the east, where some sand dunes were situated. To the south a collection of steel towers could be seen. A flame burned from the tallest one, whilst the sounds of machinery working on the site could be heard. In spite of it being desert, a black, tarmac highway ran straight across the sand towards the towers. Dark blue pipes were also to be seen, coming from various directions like giant snakes, all bound for the refinery, all carrying crude oil straight into the refinery where it would be refined into petrol, diesel, kerosene, asphalt, and chemical reagents.
Every so often a petrol tanker would speed past on its way from the refinery to the nearest town, fifty miles away. In the other direction a large, silver car sped past going towards the towards the towers. When it reached the settlement, a red and white pole was jutting out across the road blocking its progress. A guard stepped out in front of the car, a sub machine gun slung over his shoulder. The driver of the silver car lowered his window and flashed an identity card in front of the guard. He immediately turned round and nodded his head. Straight away the barrier was lifted and the car sped off into the refinery complex.

In this event-capture you can see what happens when humans manage to get "crude oil" from under the ground. They have done this by drilling down into the ground and then sucking up the oil, which has then been taken to an oil refinery where it is split up into various parts with "petroleum" being the main part of the oil. To do this a lot of humans spend many hours looking for suitable parts of Planet Earth where they can find this crude oil. They then buy the land it is under from the land owner or in some cases move the humans already living there off the land.

Petroleum, or crude oil, as it is known in some areas of the Earth, has only been used recently on a large scale in human time but it has help to revolutionise travel all over the Earth. This is because petrol oil has become the main fuel for the human vehicles of cars, lorries, buses, and so on. Coupled with this is the use of tarmac to build the roads that connect all these places around the Earth. Like coal, petroleum can be burnt and this powers the internal combustion engines in these motorised vehicles, but at the same time it gives off waste material in the form of exhaust gases. These are mainly carbon dioxide and are of no use to the humans.

Again, the amount of exploitation by the humans has left some places empty where the oil has been sucked out of the ground so other new areas have to be found to extract the oil. Some humans have seen the danger in this and have protested and tried to change the minds of those who do this, but those who own the oil companies do not want to listen at this present time. Instead, they keep drilling for more oil even in very faraway places like under the sea or in frozen lands.

I must briefly mention the fossil fuel of "natural gas", which like crude oil is sucked out of the ground and burnt as a fuel. Again, holes are bored into the ground and the natural gas that has formed over a long period of time is taken from underneath the ground and then distributed around the planet and burnt to create power and heat for both human homes and human industries. Closely connected with natural gas is "shale gas" which is also extracted from beneath the ground by a method called "fracking", where the gas is released from its pace inside the rocks by exploding the rock and capturing the gas as it escapes. Not only is this process dangerous, but it leads to the ground above collapsing and the natural water there becoming contaminated. Many humans have seen the folly of this and have stopped it from happening in their countries, but some countries still use this method to get fossil fuels.

All this burning of these fossil fuels has resulted in a major problem for the planet. The temperature of the planet is rising, which is causing the ice at the two Poles and elsewhere on the planet to melt. This in turn has caused the sea levels to rise around the planet, which in turn had led to flooding. But it has also affected the planet's weather with not only flooding, but also fires and higher temperatures in virtually every place on the planet. This has affected the animals, fish, insects, and the vegetation of Planet Earth so much that they don't know which of the four seasons they are living through and are all disorientated.

But there is one other type of fuel which the humans use, which isn't a fossil fuel and doesn't cause the Earth's temperature to rise, but is more dangerous than the fossil fuels, and we will look at that now.

Nuclear power

Location – Ukraine: a nuclear power station control room

In the control room everything was quiet. The supervisor looked at his watch. Only another hour to go before his shift ended. Time seemed to be dragging today. Over in the main reactor plant, one of the technicians was carefully transferring some used uranium rods from the reactor into the waste container. The supervisor was watching him on the monitor up on the wall in front of him.
Suddenly, the alarm sounded and everyone started running round in panic.
"What is going on?" shouted the technician. I can't leave what I'm doing!"
The supervisor radioed through to control,
"What on earth is happening?" he shouted into his radio in panic.
"We don't know!" came the reply. "It might be a false alarm, but we need to do some checks".

Meanwhile, the technician was urgently trying to finish his task with the rods but was having trouble concentrating.
The supervisor nervously looked up at the monitor half hoping to see that the rods were safely in the container, but the technician was nowhere near finished.
All the while the alarm was sounding and red lights were flashing.

This other type of power is known as "nuclear power" and it depends on nuclear fission which produces energy to make electricity, but it gives off radioactive waste. The humans have only recently discovered how to do this in their history but again it is a dangerous thing to do. They have discovered how to create nuclear fission from a mineral called "uranium" which will create electricity, but really they are like babies playing with fire here. Whilst there is no carbon left in this process, the radioactive waste is much more of a problem for the planet.

They have built nuclear power stations in different parts of the world which can produce lots of electricity, but they haven't learnt yet how to control them properly. The result has been some power stations have blown up and the radioactive nuclear elements have leaked out into the Earth's atmosphere and made some of the humans very ill or it has even killed them. Then there is another problem which they have not solved – what to do with the nuclear waste which they create in these power stations. At this moment in time, they put it into water, but even then it sometimes escapes or contaminates other water. It is buried under ground but will not decompose for up to a million years of earth time.

Worse still the humans have learnt to use this nuclear technology in a negative way and have created nuclear weapons which have the potential of destroying the planet and stopping all living beings from living on the planet. They have already used these weapons in the form of "bombs" in the activity of war and destroyed two human cities as a result.

You may think that the result of all this destruction would have helped the humans to see what a negative thing they did. But since then, they have continued to develop these nuclear weapons and make more and more of the nuclear bombs. So that now there are thousands of these nuclear bombs that the humans have created, just waiting to be used if just one human being decided to use one of them on another country. In fact, in the early days when these bombs first came into use there were just two human countries who had them. Now there are nine countries who have them and this is could increase even more making the risk of nuclear war quite likely.

Renewable energy

There is some hope coming out of this madness as some of the human beings have realised that you can get the planet's energy needs from the natural resources that surround the Earth, which are never used up. These include the wind, the water and the sun. The humans have started to realise that if the Earth is to survive these "renewable" forms of energy need to be used more and more, whilst the fossil burning fuels need to stop being used. So, they have developed various contractions which can harness these natural energy resources including solar panels, wind farms and hydro-electric power stations.

There are other things that some of the humans are doing that are helping to destroy the planet and I will show you these now.

Deforestation

Location – Indonesia: a forest being cleared by illegal loggers

The two orangutans were swinging high above the forest canopy – a scene which had not changed for thousands of years. They grabbed the branches of the trees as fast as they could as the fled in terror from the noise they could hear further away in the forest. It was illegal loggers who were cutting down the tress as quickly as possible in this remote area.

It was a well-organised activity with some men cutting the trees down, whilst another group cut the branches off those that had been felled. Yet more men took the branches out of the way so that two lorries could be moved into position, where the trunks would be lifted onto their bodies, before being secured and driven away to the logging factory over a hundred miles away.

Within an hour it was all quiet again and no one arriving at the scene would know who had done this destruction or when. A day or two later, locals would move in and burn the remaining stumps that the loggers had left behind, taking care to do it at night. Then the virgin land would be cleared and ploughed up and palm oil saplings would be planted in the place of the ancient trees. Meanwhile the orangutans would be miles away, traumatised at the loss of their habitat and wondering what could happen to them next.

The collection of wood from forests has been happening on Earth for a long time and the humans have used this wood for building and heating their homes. But in the more recent past, the constant cutting down of trees in forests for "logging" has been a problem for the humans. Due to the huge demand for wood to make furniture and paper, and for its use in building houses, more and more trees have been chopped down. Many of these have been in what the humans call "virgin forests", which are forests that have been there for millions of years.

The forests have also been chopped down to make way for land on which to grow crops on like palm oil, as in the above event-capture, or for the grazing of cattle. When the land that was once a forest is cleared by the humans it is burnt which causes much pollution in the sky from the burning smoke. But more importantly the trees which are cut down are not replaced by growing more trees elsewhere on the planet and so the ecosystem of the planet is breaking down. Many birds and animals lose their homes, and in some cases whole groups of humans who have lived in the forests for thousands of years lose their homes and their whole way of life to the humans who want to chop the trees down.

What most of the humans have not learnt yet is that if you take from the Earth, you should put it back somewhere else, otherwise you are gradually destroying the planet.

The next event-capture is showing you what is happening in many parts of the world where the waste from all this exploitation is not being reused or cleared away properly. The waste becomes something called "pollution" and this again is gradually destroying Planet Earth.

Pollution

Location - Lagos, Nigeria: the estuary of the Ogun River

Looking south from the port of Lagos you could see dozens of ships for miles out to sea. They were all moored up in deep water hoping that safety in numbers would protect them from the gangs of pirates that made frequent raids against the ships. They would come out of the various gullies and channels in the large swamp that made up the Ogun's estuary. Yet they weren't the only inhabitants who lived in this area. There were many thousands of families all trying to make an honest living from their homes built on stilts over the muddy marshland. Many caught fish that somehow managed to survive in the black waters. Others had learnt to siphon off oil from the various pipes that led to the water's edge from the oil refineries dotted around the edge of the swamp. In their efforts to take the oil, numerous leaks had occurred, leading to the blackened estuary waters. But that wasn't the only pollutant in those waters. Many factories further upstream had deposited their waste which included iron, manganese, and phosphor. All this was mixed with raw sewage that the locals left here as it was their own toilet. Yet unbelievably many still used the estuary as a source of their drinking and washing water.

In this event-capture you can see the effects of waste from the planet which the humans have allowed to occur. They have let the various waste materials flow down the river towards the sea, not bothering to dispose of it responsibly. Then the humans have used the river as a means of taking away their human waste, yet they are still drinking the life-giving water, even though it may well be poisonous and carrying all sorts of viruses and diseases. Finally, those who have broken into the pipelines carrying oil have caused more damage to the area by allowing leaks of the oil to happen. Not only do the humans living here suffer, but also any animals and fish who happen to walk, swim or fly in these parts.

This is just one example of pollution going on in one part of the Earth, yet there are thousands and thousands of other places just as bad. All over the world humans throw away paper, card, plastic and lots of other materials, either into their roadways, or into waterways, or into the seas. The result is that these places soon become clogged up with all that they have thrown away which is known as "litter". There are some humans who have decided to try and do something about this and have started picking up the litter or clearing up the mess that other humans have left behind. But sadly, most humans do not realise what they are doing and this is gradually killing many animals and fish and destroying the planet.

Exploitation of living things

In this next section of this part of my report I want to show you how the humans exploit the living things on Planet Earth. They seem to have forgotten the fact that they are just one of hundreds of thousands of living creatures on Planet Earth who all interact with each other and who respect each other's presence on Earth. There have been so many human beings over human time on Earth who have learnt to kill other creatures and have even learnt to like this activity. They do this in a variety of ways. Here is an example of this.

Hunting animals for their body parts

Location – India: a jungle game reserve *

The large male tiger slowly made its way through the thick jungle looking for a place where he could have a drink and then sleep. Its colours of orange and black merged nicely with the forest trees and bushes giving him the perfect camouflage. Kites and crickets provided the background music as he gingerly edged forward, deeper into the foliage. All of a sudden the tiger stopped and turned his head ever so slightly, as if listening for something. This was his big mistake. A shot rang out, causing the birds to scatter and scream as they went. The tiger suddenly flopped onto his side as the bullet pierced his thick skin. Within seconds three poachers appeared, all the time looking around them, suspicious of anyone nearby who had heard the gun shot. One of them put a gun to the back of the tiger's head and finished him off, once and for all.

They swiftly went to work, binding the dead tiger's legs and dragging the once magnificent beast back to their truck. Although they were taking a great risk, with severe punishment if they ever got caught, they knew the financial rewards would be worth it. The dead tiger would be taken apart bit by bit with very little left over. The skin would garner the most money, but also its bones, teeth, eyes, whiskers, claws and flesh would all contribute to humans using these parts in so called medicine.

From the above event-capture you can see some humans hunting and then killing a creature known as a "tiger". They have done this because they are able to sell its parts to other humans who want to use them as ingredients in the medicine that they create. This is just one example of hunting and killing animals on the planet. But there are many more who are killed so humans can eat their flesh. This happens to both land animals and sea creatures. They don't seem to realise that they are gradually reducing the numbers of these creatures. So many species of creature have been killed by human beings that they no longer exist on Earth. They have become what the humans call " extinct", which simply means that there are none of these creatures left on Earth.

There are many more types who are "endangered" which means that there are few of these creatures still alive on Earth and these too could become extinct in the near future. These include the land creatures which the humans call tigers, rhinoceros, gorillas, elephants, orangutan, and leopards. Then there are many others that live in or near the waters of the planet including whales, dolphins, penguins, turtles, and sharks. Apart from the creatures there are lots of living plants, trees and coral areas that are also in danger of not surviving due to the humans not caring or realising that they are gradually dying.

However, there are some humans who do see what could happen to all this wildlife, both animal and plant, on Earth. They are trying to stop the hunters and poachers and find other sources of food for the humans. They are also saving many of these creatures by placing them in specially built places where they can be looked after and be kept safe from the hunters and poachers who want to kill them. Plus, humans can learn about their existence on Earth. Here is an example of one of them.

Zoos

Location - Berlin, Germany: the city zoo

Mona and her mother walked through the entrance to the zoo and immediately Mona said, "I want to go and see the lirons!"

"Of course, Dear", her mother replied. "It's quite a walk. So why don't we look at some of the other animals on the way?"

The toddler nodded in agreement and the pair of them made a quick look into the reptile house. Then they dawdled at the elephant enclosure and then made a quick visit to the toilet before Mona pestered her mother again about the lions.

"We're nearly there!" she exclaimed. "Look! I can see them in the distance".

The mother pushed the buggy past the penguins and towards the Lion enclosure. A tall wire-mesh fence separated the mother and her daughter from a group of lethargic lions. The little girl sat wide-eyed as she looked at these magnificent creatures. She had seen pictures of lions in her story books at home, but now she was seeing them in the flesh for the first time. She was very excited and shouted, "Look mummy"

Liron! I can see the lirons!"as she pointed her finger to the large male, with a mane of dark, matted hair. Her mother laughed and inwardly felt glad that there was that fence protecting her precious daughter from those vicious and wild animals. One of the lions yawned and the group looking into the enclosure all laughed together. Several took snaps with their cameras, whilst others filmed them.
"Come on Mona! It's time to go and look at the tigers," said the mother.

You have just been looking at a human creation called a "zoo". It is an area where all sorts of creatures are kept in enclosed rooms and cages where they can live, but they can never be set free back to where they came from. Several years ago, different humans found that when they went to a different land than theirs there were all sorts of creatures that lived in these lands that they had never seen before. They decided that they would like to have these creatures as possessions and take them back to their own country, which is what they did. So over time many humans collected different animals from these countries and taken them back to live in their own lands, even though the creatures that they had captured were not suited to live there. As a result, many of these creatures died, but some did survive.

At first they were seen as "pets" like dogs and cats, but eventually some of these collectors built special parks and gardens where they could be looked at by other humans and zoos were born. Although there are now hundreds of zoos all over the planet, some of them are seen by humans as prisons for the animals kept there. Indeed, some animals are kept in bad conditions and develop illnesses of both their bodies and of their minds as they miss the freedom that they once had.

However, in more recent times zoos are now becoming places where animals are protected from other humans who might kill them for their body parts and meat. These zoos are now trying to preserve these animals for the future and in cases where the animals are contented they have had offspring and so have kept this group of animals going. The scientists in the zoos have also learned a great deal about how the animals behave and what is the best way to treat them.

There are other places where the animals have much bigger areas to live in called safari parks and reserves and again the animals have seemed happier in these places, although they are many miles away from their ancestral homes.

Exploitation of humans

Apart from human beings exploiting the Earth, they also have exploited other human beings without thought for those human's welfare and state of mind. On our planet this seems unthinkable yet on Planet Earth this has been happening for many years. These humans who do this do not have any love in them and they rely on the human emotion of fear to control the other humans. Let me show you how this happens.

Child Labour

Many of the youngest humans have a pleasant early life with enough food to eat, clothes on their bodies, a house to live in, a school to educate them and loving parents to protect them. However, there are many young humans which we know as children who do not have such a life. These children are exploited by some humans and so do not have all of the benefits in life that the majority of children have. Let me show you some of these children.

Location – Democratic Republic of the Congo: the entrance to a cobalt mine

Grace, aged eight, stood patiently outside the mine entrance waiting for her brother to come back up to the surface. The air was thick with the dust of heterogenite stones which were being sorted on the surface by hundreds of creuseurs, the locals who worked in the cobalt trade. They ranged from aged six to forty-five all working in the hot sun trying to make a living from mining cobalt in this part of Africa. Eve's brother, Samuel, who was three years older than her had been down

the mine for hours scratching at the rock, trying to fill his sack with the stones which he would take back up to the surface.
It was back breaking work and dangerous too. First you had to climb down the fragile, wooden ladders to the base level. Then you had to crawl on your hands and knees for ages to get to the rock face. There was nothing to keep the tunnels secure from collapsing, and collapse they did on a regular basis, injuring and killing scores of children who were desperate to get some dollars to help their struggling families. Finally, you had to work all day, straining your eyes with just the minimum of light from a candle or torch. Plus, you had to battle with the constant dust coming off the rocks as they were chipped away from the rock face. All this to create rechargeable lithium batteries for millions of people's mobile phones the world over.
Once Samuel was back at the surface, Grace took the sack off him and dragged it over the moon-like waste land to the nearby lake, which was contaminated with the waste materials. Here, she washed each stone so that she would have a better chance of getting a good price from the foreign buyers who would pay her a pittance, before the stones were refined into crude cobalt hydroxide. This would then be shipped back to their country where it would be sold as cobalt to various hi-tech manufacturing companies who made billions from the process.

The first group of humans that are exploited to be used by other humans are children. At this age they should be attending school, but there are no schools near to where they live. Plus, as they are living in poverty, they need to get some sort of money to pay for the food which they so desperately need. As the land that they live on is over valuable minerals, other humans have come to these areas and began to exploit the natural resources found here.

This activity where the humans dig deep into the ground to get the minerals is called "mining" and is used all over the world. The names of the minerals apart from the one I mentioned above include gold, silver, copper, platinum, zinc, copper, nickel, iron, and diamonds. Although many adult humans are working in mines to bring these precious metals and minerals to the surface, there are still a large number of children doing this. Many of them would like to go to school, but they are so poor that that have to work from an early age to help bring in money for their families.

Of course, in any human activity that involves taking something from the Earth, money has been the big motivator for the humans. Whilst those doing the hard, back-breaking work get very little money, those humans further up the chain make a lot of money as the event-capture is showing. These humans do not seem to have any empathy for those humans that they exploit and in many case these humans at the mine face are little more than what the humans call "slaves". Let me explain about slaves and slavery now.

Slavery

Location - Eastern Myanmar: a woman enslaved in a call centre

"Good morning Sir! And how are you today?" said the young Thai woman in the call centre. Although she sounded bright and cheerful, inwardly she was in despair, hating what she was doing and wishing that there was some way out.

"Fine", replied the middled aged American man. "How about you?"

"Yes, I'm OK", she replied jovially, knowing she was constantly being watched by her masters, who would beat her if she didn't do what they wanted.

"I see that your profits have gone up massively since we last spoke", she said.

"That's' great news!" said the American man. "I can see the graph here in front of me on the screen".

"Well, how about investing another $500 dollars today? I'm sure that money will triple in just a few weeks", she lied, knowing that she had to keep getting as much money out of her victim for her crime lords.

She was doing this as she had been enslaved by criminals after she had answered a fake advert on a social media page which advertised well paid jobs in Thailand working for the

government for those who had computer skills and a good educational background. She fitted the bill perfectly and was taken in even more when she had an on line face to face interview with a man who made all these promises, which seemed too good to be true.

Yet when she was picked up at the airport and taken by car with a couple of other girls she soon found out what was going to happen to her. Men armed with rifles took away her passport and phone and she was forced to get in a boat and cross a river and enter Myanmar where she become a slave in a compound with no escape. Her life was now that of a human trafficked slave who had been taught to scam potential investors of all their savings by investing in fake cryptocurrency schemes. Oh! how she wished she'd listened to her instincts.

You may find this hard to understand, but there are some human beings on Planet Earth at this time who take over other human beings and force them to work for them against their will. They become what the humans call "slaves" and they are not allowed to stop doing this work until the human in control of their lives allows them to do so, or when they stop being humans.

This action has been occurring on Planet Earth for a very long time. It occurs because some humans take advantage of the innocence of some humans and they are able to trick them into believing them as in the event-capture. Yet when they go to a certain place they are captured or taken prisoner and cannot escape, unless the capturer allows them to go, or "sets them free". Once they have been captured they are forced to work in various ways that the capturers say they have to. This work can be all sorts of things and even though they do not want to do this work, the slaves have to do what the owners say otherwise they will hurt them or even kill them.

Slavery has happened all over the world in every country and has led to many humans being moved around the world in large numbers. This happened in a large way when many millions of humans were taken as slaves from the continent of Africa across the sea to the continents of America. They had to work on the land in places known as "plantations" and many of these humans died either on the journey or through being ill-treated in their work.

Eventually some humans managed to stop these humans being slaves and they were set free. But many humans are still used as slaves on the planet in the present time, even though most humans say it shouldn't be allowed to happen.

Once again, there are some groups of humans who are trying to set these human slaves free. But those who want to keep the humans working for them as slaves try to stop them. They keep them as they get a lot of money from the work that the slaves are doing for them. It is a problem that will not end until enough humans decide to stop it.

Torture

There are other humans who are also held captive by different groups of humans. This time they are undergoing a human invention called "torture". This event-capture will show you how it works.

Location – Tehran, Iran: inside a secret government building *

The prisoner was woken from his sleep. He had no idea whether it was day or night, yet he was exhausted, He had lost count of the number of times he had been interrogated and was getting near to breaking point. Once again his captors came bursting into his cell, laughing and joking in a sadistic way. They put the inevitable bag over his head and quickly pulled his arms behind his back, fixing them together and putting on tight handcuffs that cut into his wrists. Then he was half dragged and half pushed along the corridor to that hateful room where he knew he would receive no mercy and plenty of blows to every part of his body. He grew tense and tried to struggle, but he had hardly an ounce of strength left inside him.

In no time at all he was sitting down on the iron chair and the hood was lifted from him, All he could see was a piercing light. He heard the voice of the interrogator, but he could never see him. The light blinded him and he had to look away.

An iron bar smashed into his left shin and he cried out in pain.
"Welcome back my friend!" said the voice in a mocking way.
"There's plenty more of that if you don't co-operate with us"
he said menacingly. "But if you do, think of where you could
be. Far away from here and living a normal life again. Now
tell me..."
"Fuck off!" shouted the prisoner. The reaction was immediate
with the iron bar striking the back of his head, with enough
force to knock him unconscious. but almost immediately a
bucket of water was thrown over him to wake him up again.
The torture was just beginning.....

This event-capture is showing what is known as "torture"
taking place. This is where a human being will be tied up and
hit and hurt in many ways by other humans. They do this as
they want to get some information from him which he will not
tell them, they want to get him to confess to an action which
he may or may not have done. I know it may seem
unbelievable that humans treat each other in this way, when
everyone on our planet is so respectful of each other, but this
what some humans do to other humans on Planet Earth.
They say they do it because the human they are torturing may
be a criminal who has committed a crime, but in most cases it
will be for a different reasons. This could be because he is not
of the same belief as the torturers, or he has demonstrated
against them or has written something that they didn't like or
agree with. These are just some of the many reasons for
torture, but unfortunately those who do the torturing often
enjoy and like what they doing and do not have any guilty
feelings about it.
As with slavery, there are some humans who are trying to stop
this from happening and they tell the rest of the humans what
is going on. But most humans do not bother or worry about
this and do nothing. So, the torture continues in many places
on Earth.

Another way that humans control other humans is by watching
them in secret and seeing what they are doing. Here is an
example of that.

Surveillance

Location – Ouagadougou, Burkina Faso, Africa: the bedroom of a house

In the cramped bedroom of the small house, the two men were discussing their plan to blow up a prominent government building. Their minds were inflamed with hatred for what the government had been doing to their country. They were fed up with debate. They wanted action as they believed that this was the only way to achieve change. They saw themselves as freedom-fighters, standing up for the rights of their fellow human beings. The government on the other hand saw them as terrorists and would stop at nothing to halt their campaign of terror.
Little did the two men know, but their every move was being watched on a large monitor several miles away in a top secret government building. Every word they said and every movement they made was being recorded. A government spy had been into the flat above when they were out and had installed a tiny secret camera that looked down from the ceiling on them. The anti-terrorist squad had seen the piles of explosives that they had taken into the house and knew exactly where they were. They had listened in on every telephone conversation they had made in the last month. They knew what their favourite foods were and they knew just who they had met outside the house. They were now nearly ready to strike and put an end to the plans.

Humans love to watch what other humans are doing and especially when they think they are doing something that they shouldn't be doing. But sometimes some humans will "spy" on other humans by looking at them without them knowing it. This can be malicious such as a male human watching a female human when she doesn't know it. Or watching another human being's home so that when they leave their home, so they can enter it to steal goods from that human's home.

Sometimes, as in the event-capture, humans from the government of a country will secretly watch what some other humans are doing in order to stop them doing something which might hurt lots of other people. They say that this is allowed for security reasons, but some humans don't like this idea and think that governments are spying on ordinary people who haven't done anything wrong. In fact, many places on Earth have what are known as CCTV cameras operating which can film what humans are doing. They might be able to catch criminals, but a lot of the time they are just filming other humans for no reason at all.

Finally, I will show you some humans who live and work in secret from other humans.

Secret humans

Location – Nevada, USA: a military air base

The coach left a trail of dust and broken stones as it negotiated the bumpy dirt track towards the top secret military complex. Its motley crew of passengers included scientists, engineers, and military personnel, all bound for the base. All of them had Level 5 security clearance, but very few of them knew each other. No one spoke to each other as the coach chugged along. They had all convened at a hotel on the outskirts of Las Vegas two hours earlier and been checked onto the coach after being thoroughly searched and vetted.
Soon it arrived at the edge of the base. It was whisked through the outer gates by two soldiers, one on either side of the dusty road.
Then it came to a complete stop further inside the base, at a second set of gates. Everyone got off as they had done many times before. They went into a passage way where they had to show their laminate passes to a security guard, who thoroughly looked at their faces and the picture on the pass. For each passenger, he scanned their pass and a beep went up from his scanner. All the items in their pockets were emptied. Belts, shoes and their bags were put on a conveyor belt which

*went through a different scanner. They then were checked by
two more guards with metal detectors for anything else hidden
in their clothes. Finally, they were then let into the base
proper.*

*In front of them beige coloured buildings could be seen, many
of them with antenna on the top. The noise of low flying jets
could be heard in the distance and the wind blew sand and
dust around their feet. Walking along to their next mode of
transport, they were surrounded by heavily armed soldiers
who watched them intently. The atmosphere was eerie to say
the least. They walked in different directions to four mini
buses, which would take them to their assigned places of work.
It was well paid of course, but they were aware that they were
being observed, not just at the base, but also when they were
at home on leave. So, they never really relaxed. If only those
in the outside world really knew what was going on in that
base, their hair would stand on end!*

There are some human groups that I must tell you about before
I finish my report. These are humans who work in "secret",
which means that other humans do not know about what they
do or who they are. Yet I can see them and they are living in
fear as they do not want the rest of the humans to find out
what they are doing.

Many of them live and work in special bases they have built
underground in remote areas, or in military bases where only
certain types of humans are permitted to enter, These are
found all over the world and are kept secret from the vast
majority of the other human beings. Those who work there
must promise never to reveal anything about what they are
doing, otherwise they or their members of their families could
be killed. So, they are kept in a state of fear for revealing
anything about what is going on in these places. Yet, there are
some humans who have spoken about these places as they
think that the other humans should know what is going on in
them.

'What are they keeping secret from the rest of the humans?'
you may ask. Well, all sorts of experiments and research are
taking place in these secret bases. As I mentioned earlier other
races from other places in the universe have made contact

many times during the time that humans have been on Earth. The humans who are in the military, or part of the governments of some countries know about this contact and have worked with various races not from Earth in their experiments and research. However, there will come a day when all that is hidden from the other humans will be revealed.

Now, we are nearly at the end of my report. The final part is next and in it I conclude all that I have seen on Planet Earth and where I think the humans are heading.

Part 12

Human Future

Don't it always seem to go?
That you don't know what you've got,
'Til it's gone

The End of Human Life

Location – Oxford, England: a funeral taking place

"Ashes to ashes, dust to dust," said the priest in a deep booming voice, making sure that everyone in the crematorium could hear. Most of the mourners were looking at the light brown wooden coffin lying on the dais, covered in a large wreath of pink chrysanthemums and white lilies. Virtually everyone there was wearing black clothing of some sort, as was the tradition for funerals in this part of the world. On the front row, two of the ladies were weeping quietly, every now and then wiping a tear away. A portly man sitting in between two ladies put each of his arms around their shoulders and whispered something into the ear of the lady sitting on his right. She looked towards him and smiled briefly, before wiping her eyes once more.
"We shall now sing the hymn, "All things bright and beautiful" announced the priest, "As we say our final goodbyes to Elaine."
With that, the mourners all stood up and the organist played the opening notes of the hymn. Most of the mourners joined in with the singing, though some of the younger mourners

remained silent. When it came to the third verse, the coffin started to slide slowly into an opening at the back of the crematorium. The two women on the front row began to weep uncontrollably as the coffin of their dead mother moved gradually out of sight.....

For the final event-capture in my report I want to show you what happens to the vessel known as the human body when the human has finally left the planet. In every different part of the planet the humans have some sort of ceremony to say farewell to that particular human being. In some places it is a joyful occasion with lots of colour and dancing. In other places it is a sad affair with many humans crying as they are sad at its departure, and many wear black for the ceremony which is called a "funeral".

Once the main ceremony is completed, the body can be burnt and the remnants, the "ashes", are given to the human's family to either keep, or to throw on the land or the sea if they wish. Or in other cases, the body is placed into the ground where it is covered with the soil of the Earth. This place is known as a "grave" and may have a stone with writing placed by it, so the friends and family of the human can go and remember or even communicate with the human who has left the Earth.

So, that is the end of all the event-captures that I have made on my visit to the planet, where I have observed human life on Planet Earth from the beginning – birth, right through its various forms to the end – death. But now it is time to sum up the report of my visit and my observations of human beings. It has been a very interesting visit to say the least.

Human Ignorance

Firstly, I would conclude that the human beings are a strange race from what I have observed and experienced. They exist in all different shapes, sizes, and colours. Not like in some other parts of the universe where they all look and dress the same. Of course, some human beings use this as an opportunity to spread dissent and disharmony amongst the rest of the humans by emphasising their differences, rather than their similarities. However, many humans are interested in making friends with other humans and enjoy moving around the planet in various ways to see how other humans live, just like me!

Next, I have come to see that most humans don't seem to realise what they are doing on the planet and all the opportunities it gives them for growth and evolution. I have learnt that the humans' purpose is to evolve and experience life on Planet Earth with all the various possibilities it gives them. Some do grow more spiritual and closer to Source whilst they are on the planet, but for many of them it is a wasted opportunity. These humans have yet to learn to share and communicate with other human beings more and let their differences be a source of wonder and appreciation.

They also need to learn to appreciate all the various living forms they share the planet with and to respect the land they live on. Yet many humans have evolved to become more selfish and fearful, especially with the notion of other humans taking their possessions. Also, in many countries they don't have the respect for the elders any more, even though they have lived longer and know more than they will ever know.

From all the observations I have made of the human beings, one of the most important is that it would seem many of them are constantly divided from each other. Whilst you can see that at various times in their time on Earth humans have worked together, especially in the early days, yet in recent times they have become more divided than ever. Individual humans seem to fight against each other, either with their bodies, or with their minds, which causes more "apartness" between them. Then when this attitude and mind-set is extended to whole nations this manifests itself in the human creation called war.

Also, most humans are not aware of the hidden energies that exist in and around Planet Earth. There are many of these energies, such as sound waves, micro waves, light waves, ultra violet light and even more that they haven't discovered yet. These are things which can't be seen by the humans with their normal vision range or noticed by their other senses. Yet they are there all the time, affecting the human's wellbeing and health. They need to learn how to be aware of these energies and what they can do to the human body. If they do this they will be able to be more healthy and their bodies will function as they are meant to.

Human Selfishness

I have also discovered that on Earth there are two basic things that humans use to exist – air and water. The air is there all around you and moves in and out of humans and is called "breathing". This is the basic life process on earth and without it the humans would die. The other thing is water, which like air moves into and out of the human body. In fact, most of the human body is made up of water, apart from the flesh and bones which hold it together. Humans can live without taking in water for much longer than air, but if they don't take in these two ingredients they stop living on Earth.

Sadly though, over time some humans have corrupted the water on Earth from its pure form and destroyed the life force within it. This has been done by adding different substances to it that were never designed to be put into water. The humans call this destruction, "pollution" and while the water can deal with these substances up to a point, the water has its limits and these limits have been reached in many areas of the Earth. The life force in the water has expired and the creatures that once lived in the water have stopped living.

Pollution isn't just about destroying the water though. It can also refer to the human poisoning of the air and the ground. This is mainly done by extracting fossil fuels like oil, coal and gas from under the ground and then burning them to create energy. These all naturally occur inside the Earth, but many humans have removed so much of them that less and less of them remain. You can see how primitive these actions are, but the humans with the power and influence want this method to continue, even though there are plenty of harmless and natural ways of creating energy, which they urgently need to discover and eventually use.

The other important observation I have made about the humans is that they operate at different levels of existence.

Some live very basic lives of just existing as humans. They do not have any possessions, or money or a home, but live in the forests, just like many animals do. They do not have any need for money as they use what is naturally occurring there. Plus, they share all their food and treat everyone the same. Yet many humans who live in this way are dying out as other humans take over their lands and chop down the forests.

The other humans who do have the three things I mentioned – money, possessions, and homes – all in excess in some cases, do not like to share what they have with other humans who haven't got enough food or money to live in the same way that they do. These humans have become greedy and selfish and constantly live in fear of losing what they have. This is on the material level of course.

Yet on the mind level, humans can also operate at different levels. Some operate in ignorance of what life is all about and just live their lives as if they were in a dream or a play. They have no idea of why they are on Earth and what they should be doing with their lives. They too have become greedy and selfish and fearful. In many cases they have become trapped by their body's needs. Apart from the basic human needs such as air, food, sleep, they seem to have an overwhelming desire to have something that they don't really need.

From my report you can see several of these so called "needs" in action. These may include smoking, alcohol, and certain types of food, clothes, possessions, buildings, other human beings, money, violence, revenge, sex and drugs. They are known as "addictions" which is a condition whereby the human believes that he or she needs to have this item or this experience, no matter what it might do them, or the other humans around them. Unless the human manages to stop this desire or addiction, it will ultimately stop them being a human being and make them less than human. That is why so many of the humans are living lives that make them unhappy, or jealous, or angry or worried.

On the other hand, there are a few human beings who understand why they are living as humans on Planet Earth. They are at peace with themselves and with other humans and understand what they should be doing with their human lives. They are not sleeping, but are awake and have woken up from the dream that other humans are in. They understand how life works and that life has a purpose and have made the best use of all the opportunities that life on Earth brings them. Money is no longer important to them, as are possessions. Instead of taking they are giving and feeling much more positive inside and peaceful as well. They are calm and contented and settled and have an inner peace which cannot be brought about through possessions. They are able to live their lives as was planned and take each experience they face as something to learn from.

Fear and Love

Next, I would say that the humans seem to be developing at different levels of understanding from the very primitive to the very enlightened. This is on a scale from extreme fear through to complete love. Many adult humans have lost the joy that they once had inside them as children. They fail to see the beauty that is all around them on the Earth. Instead, they have become preoccupied with bringing money into their lives. They have become obsessed with accumulating meaningless possessions. In some cases, they have become slaves to other humans who exploit them into doing things that they don't really want to do. Yet they have to do them in order to be paid money, so that they can buy the things which were once free to all human beings. Yet now most humans are "owned" by a select few who control the distribution of things like money, food, entertainment and power. So, it would seem that the majority of humans are exploited by a minority of other humans who are using the tool of money to keep them under control.

In other words, they are living in "fear". They are afraid of what might happen to them. The fear they won't have enough money coming into their lives, or the fear they won't have enough food to eat, or a house to live in, and so on. Sometimes the humans are in fear of what other humans might do to them through violence, or conflict, or war. This fear is then passed onto their children or other members of their family, or onto their friends, and so the fear grows and grows and becomes exaggerated. So, the humans become more separate from each other.

The opposite of this is living in "love", where there is no fear in the humans who live like this. They show love to everyone around them, even if some humans are aggressive or hateful towards them. The love they show can then be passed onto all the different humans they come into contact with and as a result it spreads throughout the planet. Indeed, most humans would prefer to live in love as opposed to living in fear if they could. But very often they let the feelings of fear take over.

Waking Up

As you can see there are a very large number of human beings who are not happy with the lives they are living. They have this feeling inside them that the way they are living their life on Earth is not right. They are unhappy with their lives. They may be struggling to find food, to find a home that they can live in, to have a job that will give them enough money to pay all their bills, to be in a loving relationship with someone. They might actually have more than enough money for their needs, they might have more than enough food to eat, or be in a loving relationship, yet they are still unhappy.

This is because they realise deep down inside them that they have not yet discovered who they really are. You can say that their role at this stage as a human being is being something that they are not. They are desperately trying to discover who they really are. This means finding out what they should be doing with their life and how they should be living their life. They can do this by asking the simple question, "Who am I?" and sooner or later they will get the answer. This in turn will lead to them "waking up" and realising who they are and what they are doing on Earth.

"How do humans wake up?" you may ask. They can do it in all sorts of ways, through all sorts of experiences. For some it might be the drudgery of their existence. They get up in the morning, go to work, come home, watch the TV and then go to bed. Then they do this the next day and the next day, until eventually they start asking the question, "Why am I doing this?" "What is life all about?" They come to realise that they are trapped in this existence and unless they choose to do something about it, everything will continue to stay the same.

For others, this awakening can occur when someone they know and love decides to leave the human body and Earth in the death process. They become heartbroken at losing someone they have loved for years or months or even just days. They look back at that person's life and ask, "What is life all about?" They ask questions of their friends or people they know who have woken up, or they read books which help them. The more they search the clearer the answer becomes.

This thought process doesn't always happen as the result of a death of human, it could happen at the end of a relationship, such as a marriage break up or a person moving away from home for the first time. Another way humans wake up is when they look at what is going on in the world. They see news programmes on the TV which show the violence of human existence where humans drop bombs on other humans, or fire bullets into them. Something in them stirs and they think this isn't natural. They understand that this might be "normal" for many humans to hurt other humans, but they see it isn't the way humanity was meant to be. Then they start asking those same questions.

Finally, there are some humans who wake up naturally. They are surrounded by love from their parents and their friends. They aren't influenced by the materialism around them. Instead, they see the beauty of Planet Earth – the sun and moon, the stars, the sky with its ever-changing colours, the mountains and the trees, the animals and birds and fish; and most of all, other humans who have woken up. They realise that being a human being has purpose and beauty and power and they start living life as it was meant to be for humans.

Conclusion

At one time humans believed that the Earth was flat, just like one giant table and that if you sailed far enough your ship would go right over the edge and into nothingness! It wasn't until one human being with vision came along to convince the mass of humanity that the Earth was in fact round. Back then humans had the belief that the Earth was at the centre of the universe and that its sun travelled round the Earth and not the other way round. Again, this belief was held by most humans until someone came along and said that it wasn't so. The Earth in fact orbited its sun and it is just a very tiny planet among lots of star systems in the Universe, each with their own set of planets.

Now at present there are many humans who think that they are the only life forms who exist in the whole of the universe, when in fact they are shown thousands of photographs and films of vehicles and their occupants from other planets in the universe. Of course, those in authority have tried to keep this knowledge from the vast majority of humans for many years, but gradually humans are starting to accept that theirs is not the only life form in the universe.

Many humans do not realise what potential they have. They are stuck in traditions and religions and laws that tell them how to live. They haven't yet learnt to think for themselves and to question everything they see or hear. So, they do not progress either as individuals, or as a species. They are like the earlier humans who only thought in one way and wouldn't accept that there was a different way to the one which they believed. Many humans are afraid of change and so close their minds to all the different possibilities of life. They stay like young humans in their minds and in their view of the world. Their minds are closed to all the different possibilities there are in human existence and do not mature into fully grown human beings.

In conclusion, it can be seen just how primitive humans are compared to us. They seem to want to destroy the planet they are living on by using up all the natural resources like the trees, the water and the earth without replacing any of these. They seem to be obsessed by their invention called money which dominates every action that they carry out as human beings. Then they seem to be permanently at war with each other, thriving on the human action called violence, having not learnt to respect and love each other. They are even planning to destroy each other through the weapons they have created.

Unlike us, they seem intent on staying divided with each other and not learning to love each other. They are obsessed by fear and trying to be better than each other, rather than trying to help each other. Many humans haven't learnt what responsibility is and how they are responsible for both the planet that they live on and the people they live with. The way for mankind to find immortality is to learn not to kill. This means stopping the things that kill – guns, bombs, weapons, vehicles, diseases, chemicals. Yet, they continue like this as if it won't come back to them in a different form. They haven't yet learnt that what you give out will come back to you. Most of them don't have a vision for the future of Planet Earth or themselves and this is quite concerning.

My conclusion is that if they continue to live and exist like this, they will not only destroy themselves, but also Planet Earth itself and then it will be too late. That is unless more humans change their way of thinking from taking to giving and sharing instead. There is still hope for human beings.

Afterword

Yes there are two paths you can go by,
But in the long run,
There's still time to change the road you're on

Location - A manned space station orbiting the Earth

It was a beautiful sight for the six human beings based on the
space station which was orbiting the Earth. They had been up
in space for almost four months now and still had two more to
go. The commander of the space station, Major Thomas
Simpson, an American, was pleased with the way the mission
was going. He got on well with his fellow astronauts – two
Russians, two Chinese, a Japanese and a South African. They
gelled together as a team, in spite of their different
nationalities and cultures. Every day when he looked down on
the Earth with its blue, green and white covering, he couldn't
help to be amazed by its wonder and power. He felt humbled
that he had been given this opportunity to live up here away
from the madness down below. Although he missed his wife
and children, the experience he was having in space far
outweighed the disadvantages of his job. At other times he
would look up into deep space and shudder when he saw all
those billions of stars, encased in the blackness which went on
and on for God knows how long. It was at times like these that
he would become almost detached from the human body that
was him. But then just as he was getting lost in his own
wonder, he would look down to Planet Earth and think of all
those billions of human beings on the surface. The Earth was
still a special place to live and exist in the Universe. There
was still hope whatever might be going on down there.
Suddenly he was woken from his day dreaming by the sound of
Mission Control calling in. As he looked down at Earth he
thought, "It is still a beautiful world".

HUMAN BEING

Acknowledgments

A big thank you to the following.
To my close family:- Wendy, Emma, Alex, Peter, Owen, Hayden and Ashley. Plus, my godfather, Roy Sullivan.
To my friends Mark, Dave and Trudi, Peter, Mike, Ian, Alan, Nigel and Lesley, John, Andy and Dave. Also, Jon, Dick, Simon, John, Ray and Robin. Also to: Chrissie Brampton, Lindsay Coulson, Angela and Andrew Donovan, David Hobbs, David Jon, Angel Joughin-Coppin, Sue Lee, Dave Sumeray, Majella and Ted Turner.

A big thank you to all the various authors and teachers who I have interviewed for my podcast, *Mark Chatterton's Look at Life*, or whose writings have had an influence on me: - Mark Boyle, Lorna Byrne, Diana Cooper, Hazel Courteney, David Ditchfield, David Hamilton, Ian Lawton, Peter Owen Jones, Anthony Peake, James Redfield, Ellis Silver, Steve Taylor, Andy Thomas, Chris Thomas, Neil Donald Walsch and Colin Wilson.
Thanks to my musician friends and those involved in the music industry, including those who I have interviewed for my podcast, *Mark Chatterton's Rock Files*:- Peter Banks, Del Bromham, Jonathan Cooke, Pete Feenstra, Nick Garner, Claire Hamill, Carvin Jones, Kevin Morris, Alan Nimmo, John Reid, Nick and Helen Sheridan, Keith Xander, John Young. Special thanks to Laurie Wisefield and Martin Turner.
Thanks to the explorers, Ben Fogel, Simon Reeves, and Levison Wood and their teams for educating me about the planet that we live in and for taking us all to places that we would never be able to go to ourselves. Thanks also to the brave investigative journalists and whistle-blowers who have exposed the various injustices, corruption and human rights abuses going on in the world today.
Thanks to the following musicians for the "moments of pleasure" they have given me for their music and lyrics:- Kate Bush, Nick Drake, Keith Emerson, Peter Gabriel, Rory Gallagher, George Harrison, Bryn Haworth, Roger Hodgson, Mick Hucknall, Tony Iommi, Michael Jackson, Greg Lake,

John Lees, John Lennon, Phil Lynott, Chris Martin, Paul McCartney, Larry Norman, Philip Oakey, Gerry Rafferty, Cat Stevens, Sting, Pete Townshend and John Wetton. Plus, all the various groups I have listened to over the years and whose gigs I have attended, including After The Fire, Barclay James Harvest, King King, Stray, Xander & the Peace Pirates and Wishbone Ash.

A special thank you to Pamela and Simon Young for their hospitality, kindness and love.

A big thank you to Simon Coote and John Norton for guidance and help along my Life's Path.

Thanks for your friendship and support Brenda, Cynthia, Julia, Jean and Chris.

To Terry Edwards and his wife June for lasting friendship

Finally, last but by no means least, a very special thank you to my two closest friends and companions on this path through Life, for help, inspiration and support:- Howard West and Ian Jones, with love and thanks.

Lyrics details

Here are the source of the lyrics I have used at the start of each chapter in the book, with the name of the song, writer/artist/group and the album which the song comes from.

Introduction:- *Reader's Digest* from the album *Only Visiting This Planet* by Larry Norman. Written by Larry Norman

Part 1:- *Skin* from the album *Valhalla* by Stray. Written by Del Bromham

Part 2:- *Time and Space* from the album *No Smoke Without Fire* by Wishbone Ash. Written by Martin Turner

Part 3:- *Like the Power of a Jet* from the album *Laser Love* by After The Fire. Written by Piercy/Banks

Part 4:- *Talk to Me* from the album *Slide Don't Fret* by Bryn Haworth. Written by Bryn Haworth

Part 5:- *African* from the album *Face to Face* by Barclay James Harvest. Written by John Lees.

Part 6:- *Telegraph Road* from the album *Love over Gold* by Dire Straits. Written by Mark Knopfler.

Part 7:- *I Love Music* from the album *Family Reunion* by The O'Jays. Written by Gamble/Huff.

Part 8:- *Baker Steet* from the album *City to City* by Gerry Rafferty. Written by Gerry Rafferty.

Part 9:- *Money* from *The Dark Side of the Moon* by Pink Floyd. Written by Roger Waters.

Part 10:- *Girl* from the album *Rubber Soul* by the Beatles. Written by Lennon/McCartney

Part 11:- *Pure and Easy* from the album *Who's Next* by the Who. Written by Pete Townshend

Part 12:- *Big Yellow Taxi* from the album *Ladies of the Canyon* by Joni Mitchell. Written by Joni Mitchell.

Postscript:- *Stairway to Heaven* from the album *Led Zeppelin IV* by Led Zeppelin. Written by Page/Plant.

About the author

Mark Chatterton is an author, broadcaster, teacher and philosopher. He has written over fifteen book on such subjects as music, education, transport and Mind, Body and Spirit. He has a degree in Theology from Oxford University. His interests include travel, music and photography. He lives in Essex, not far from London.

Website - markchatterton.com

Facebook – Mark Chatterton: author

You Tube – Mark Chatterton's Look at Life

Printed in Great Britain
by Amazon

40044051R00145